CRACKING
ANATOMY

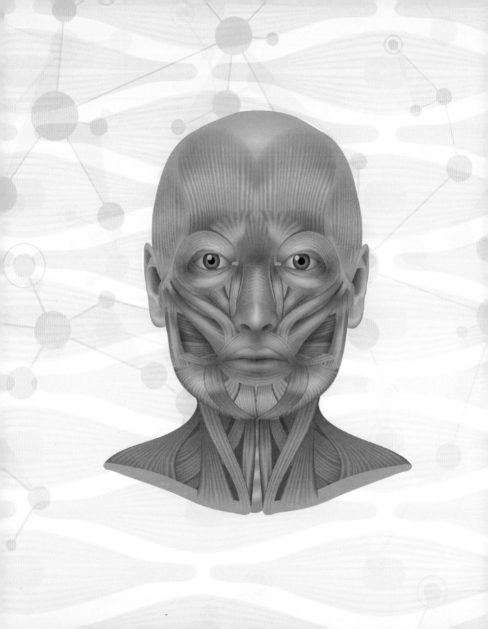

CRACKING ANATOMY

KEN OKONA-MENSAH

An Hachette UK Company
www.hachette.co.uk

First published in Great Britain in 2020 by Cassell,
an imprint of Octopus Publishing Group Ltd
Carmelite House
50 Victoria Embankment
London EC4Y 0DZ
www.octopusbooks.co.uk

Consultant: Professor Barry Mitchell
Editor: Claudia Martin
Designer: Tracy Killick
Picture Researcher: Rachel Blount
Proofreader: Katy Denny
Indexer: Vanessa Bird

ISBN 978 1 78840 151 7

A CIP catalogue record for this book is available
from the British Library.

Printed and bound in China

10 9 8 7 6 5 4 3 2 1

Publishing Director: Trevor Davies
Production Controller: Caterina Falqui
Editorial Assistant: Mireille Harper

CONTENTS

INTRODUCTION

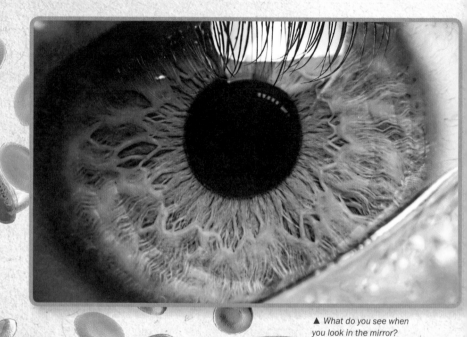

▲ *What do you see when you look in the mirror?*

Your body is an amazing machine that has evol– STOP. Do you really need someone to tell you this? If you do not know how stupendous that thing is you drag around with you every day, during the good times and the bad, then you probably should put this book down right now, go straight to the mirror and take a good long look at yourself. So, off you go.

Now that you have taken a look at yourself, how do you feel? Regardless of the answer, the fact that you are reading this book is testament to your desire to learn more about yourself – about the human condition from a physical point of view.

Whether you believe in a higher being or not is neither here nor there. The unquestionable truth here is that your body is a dynamic and intelligently designed product, that constantly interacts and learns from its environment. It comes with systems that provide the perfect examples of what it means to work together, with one sole purpose: to keep you alive.

In nature, often what happens on the micro level tends to happen on the macro level, too. With this in mind, what a wonderful thing it would be if we humans used our internal networks as mentors for how working together can be done. Imagine a world where each one of us represented a valuable, complex organ system, with one common goal: to keep our shared humanity alive.

This book will give you an insight into how your body is organized and how it works. The top and tail ends of the book put everything into context, taking you on a tour behind the scenes, so you can see how our understanding of anatomy grew to what it is today, and what we need to think about now as we step into the future. Throughout the rest of the book there is a bit of anatomy, obviously, and a bit of physiology thrown in too, because structure and function go hand in hand.

Hopefully this book will whet your appetite and get your juices flowing to help you digest, in small manageable chunks, just how truly amazing you really are.

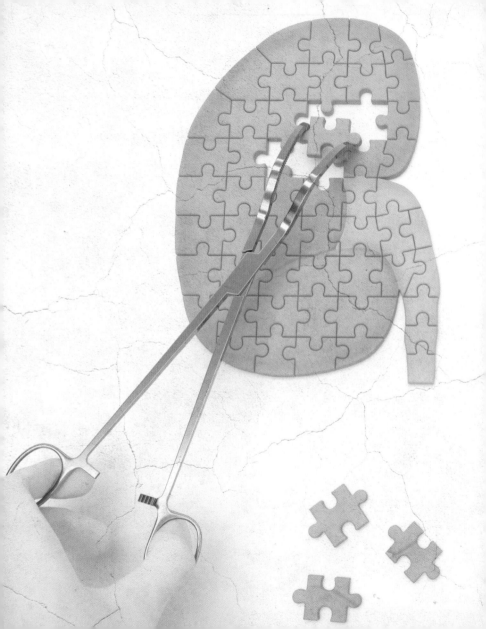

CHAPTER 1

THE FUNDAMENTALS

WHAT'S IT ALL ABOUT?

When you think of anatomy, what springs to mind? Frogs' legs, human body parts, preserved rodents spread-eagled like Leonardo da Vinci's Vitruvian Man, or medical students ferociously learning about how the iliac fossa forms at the anteromedial surface of the ilium wing? Anatomy is certainly all of the above and more.

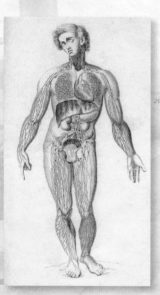

Anatomy is a branch of biology devoted to understanding what those different bits are that make you, where they fit and how your body puts it all together. Understanding anatomy is such a mammoth enterprise that it has taken us thousands of years, from the first recorded attempts by the ancients Egyptians, to get this far. Yet we have only truly mastered the basics. Furthermore, anatomy is so old, it has developed its own unique language.

MACROSCOPIC OR MICROSCOPIC

'Anatomy' is ancient Greek for 'dissection'. The science has two main branches: macroscopic and microscopic. Macroscopic, or gross, anatomy is concerned with structures that can be determined simply with your naked eye. To discriminate at a much deeper level requires the use of optical instruments and that the sample undergoes various treatments and preparations. Optical instruments become necessary when you try to distinguish between two structures that lie closer than 0.2 micrometres apart, because that is the resolving power of the retina in your eyes. The study of such

▼ *Anatomy is more than just learning about what your naked eye can see. It also includes the subject histology, which seeks to identify the structure and composition of different cells and tissues that are visible only under high magnification.*

tiny anatomical structures is termed microscopic anatomy, or histology, and is concerned with the business of tissues, cells and their organelles.

A DOSE OF PHYSIOLOGY

Anatomy is a bit lost without its twin subject, physiology. To know anatomy without it, is like writing music without ever listening to it. Physiology puts the how and why into understanding what your body is all about. It studies how everything works and why your body does what it does under normal conditions. When anatomy is combined with diagnosing and treating diseases, it grows from being purely basic and theoretical to something meatier and patient-led that forms the backbone of medicine.

STANDING ON THE SHOULDERS OF GIANTS

▶ *Ancient Egyptians preserved the internal organs of the dead in canopic jars.*

'We have been studying human anatomy since before the days of Vesalius and just when we think there can't possibly be anything left to learn or explore, the human body makes a fool out of us.' These are the words of leading anatomist and forensic anthropologist Professor Dame Sue Black. Indeed, mankind's pursuit of knowledge has been punctuated by discoveries that have changed its course like a pinball machine.

Approaches to understanding the human body varied across the ancient world. Some traditions focused on energy flows and balance, giving rise to the Ayurvedic and Chinese practices, which today still form the basis of modern alternative medicine. Others took a more empirical approach to hunt for the seat of the soul. Our understanding of the anatomical knowledge of many other civilizations is limited by their reliance on oral rather than written records. In addition, we know little of the achievements of women before

modern times. This issue is touched on further in Chapter 13.

THE ANCIENT EGYPTIANS

The ancient Egyptians were renowned for their ability to remove and preserve organs taken from the dead during the process of mummification. The heart was later returned to the body in the belief that it was the home of the soul. Although magic was the order of the day, the Edwin Smith Papyrus (c. 1600 BC) was found to have some scientific credence. Named after the person who bought it in 1862, it is believed to be the oldest known text of medical and anatomical significance.

THE ANCIENT GREEKS

The philosopher, biologist and logician Aristotle (384–322 BC) was also preoccupied with finding the den of the soul during his anatomical dissections of animals. However, it was his fellow

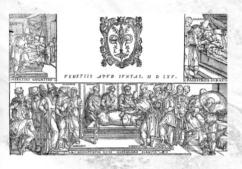

▲ *Galen is depicted dissecting a pig, at a time when dissection of human cadavers was prohibited.*

Greek scientist, Herophilos of Chalcedon (325–255 BC), who was recognized as the world's first anatomist. After studying in Alexandria, in modern Egypt, he conducted the first scientific cadaveric dissections, which were a rarity at the time since human dissections were hugely frowned upon as irreverent, as well as unclean and risky.

Another gifted Greek physician, called Galen (c. 129–c. 210 AD), followed suit to Alexandria in the 2nd century AD. Based on his animal dissections, he produced a wealth of written text that provided invaluable descriptions of the body, especially the musculoskeletal systems. He also recognized that damage to the spinal cord was associated with increasing risk of paralysis and death the higher up the damage was on the spine.

ISLAMIC SCHOLARS

Galen owes much of his later prominence to the Islamic scholars of the Middle Ages who translated and reproduced his work, as well as correcting sections from their own observations. Islamic masters of anatomy included Abdallatif al Baghdadi (1162–1231), who carried out some of the first postmortem autopsies. During the Dark Ages, intellectual leadership passed to the Middle East and remained there until the 13th century. It was not until the Renaissance kicked off in the 14th century that a new age of experimentation and investigation began in Europe.

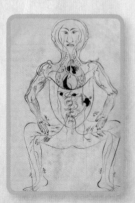

▲ *Mansur ibn Ilyas produced his colour illustrated* Anatomy *in the 15th century.*

THE RENAISSANCE YEARS

The Renaissance, between 1300 and 1600, gave life to many great artists who helped anatomy flourish with their accurate representations of the human body. Up until this point, most anatomy texts were descriptive and lacked detailed illustrations. Artists such as Leonardo da Vinci (1452–1519), Albrecht Dürer (1471–1528) and Michelangelo (1475–1564) studied corpses to create accurate images that also became an integral part of their own, and others', printed publications communicating anatomical discoveries.

The Belgian anatomist and physician Andreas Vesalius (1514–64) is often named as the father of modern anatomy. His contribution to the discipline represented a paradigm shift in the approaches used to acquire knowledge. From direct observations of cadaveric dissection, in 1543 he published his most notable work, the monograph entitled 'De humani corporis fabrica' ('On the Fabric of the Human Body'). Billed as the first great achievement of science in modern times, it introduced anatomical language that is still in use today and presented the musculoskeletal system in an inimitable way.

THE AGE OF ENLIGHTENMENT

During the Enlightenment, anatomy truly took off, leading particularly to advances in our understanding of the circulatory system. No one did so much in this area as Cambridge medical graduate William Harvey (1578–1657), who produced work that confirmed earlier suggestions by Islamic scholar Ibn al-Nafis (1213–88) that there were two circulations, in which blood went first to the lungs and then to the rest of the body. Often referred to as the father of physiology, Harvey also implanted the idea that fertilization of an egg by sperm was necessary for reproduction to occur.

▼ Vesalius's ground-breaking book contained detailed illustrations of the muscular system.

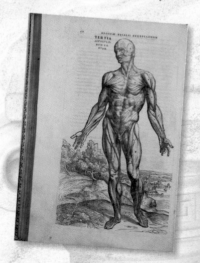

GREAT ANATOMISTS

CENTURY		REGION	NOTABLE FIGURES	CONTRIBUTION TO ANATOMY
BC	16th	Egypt, Africa	High-ranking officials	Produced the Edwin Smith Papyrus, the first known medical and anatomical reference. Believed the heart was the seat of intelligence
	4th	Greece, Europe	Aristotle, philosopher	Coined the term 'anatomy' after dissecting small animals
	3rd	Egypt, Africa	Herophilos of Chalcedon, physician	Was the first to perform a public human dissection and recognized the importance of the brain and nerves as the 'seat of intelligence'
	2nd	Greece, Europe	Galen of Pergamon, physician	Produced written work that became the standard text for around 14 centuries. Seen as the father of modern medicine
AD	8th–13th	Arab World, Middle East	Islamic scholars including Muhammad ibn Zakariya al-Razi, Ibn Sina, Ibn al-Nafis, and Abdallatif al-Baghdadi	Saved vast knowledge from disappearing after the fall of the Roman Empire and corrected many of Galen's descriptions from their own observations
	16th	Italy, Europe	Andreas Vesalius, anatomist	Published the influential 'On the Fabric of the Human Body', gave us terms such as the mitral valve, and uniquely illustrated muscles and bones. Demonstrated that many earlier texts were inaccurate. Seen as the father of modern-day anatomy
	17th	Italy, Europe	Marcello Malpighi, physician	Identified capillaries as the vessels that link arteries and veins in the lungs of frogs
	17th	England, Europe	William Harvey, physician	Published 'An Anatomical Study of the Motion of the Heart and of the Blood in Animals', which correctly described how blood was pumped around the body

CADAVERS AND CRIMINALS

Over the centuries, anatomy has had a fraught relationship with cadavers. While clearly being an essential resource in educating physicians past, present and future, outside the medical field the dissection of cadavers has historically evoked a negative reaction. Aside from spiritual concerns and fears over the potential health risks, the public's unease with the practice is somewhat vindicated when you consider that anatomy has a dark past.

Most early anatomists improved their knowledge by dissecting animals that were either dead or, sometimes, alive. Although extremely useful, not all the information could be confidently extrapolated to humans. Dissecting a human body provided a more accurate and trustworthy source of information. During the 18th and early 19th centuries in Europe and the United States, as medical training establishments grew, there was a growing demand for dead bodies. Yet, at the time, the only legal

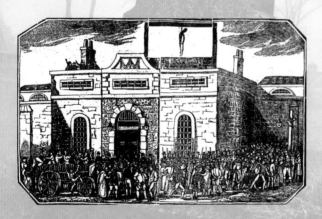

◀ William Burke was hanged in 1829 for the murder of 15 people whose bodies he sold to the anatomist Robert Knox for dissection. In a twist of fate, after his execution, Burke's body was immediately used for anatomical dissections. His skeleton is on public display at Edinburgh University Museum.

▶ *This photograph of the Anatomy Department at Cambridge University was taken around 1890.*

source of cadavers was the penal system, which fed the bodies of executed criminals to medicine as a final act of retribution. Where there is demand, there is money to be made, fuelling the black market trade in human remains.

GRAVE ROBBERS

As a result of this demand, thieves regularly stole freshly buried corpses, especially those of the poor and disenfranchized, to sell them to medical schools. In the United States, enslaved and free African Americans were particularly at risk of grave robbing. On both sides of the Atlantic, the 'body-snatching' industry became a lucrative enterprise for so-called 'resurrectionists'. The bodies of infants were considered a highly prized commodity as most penal-system cadavers were male and little was known about how humans developed. Some medical schools were even deliberately located within body-carrying distance of graveyards. Depraved individuals, notably Edinburgh's William Burke and William Hare, actually murdered to keep up supplies. Naturally, once the public got wind of these horrors, there was outrage.

ANATOMY ACTS

With the passing of the United Kingdom's Anatomy Act in 1832, executed murderers no longer received eternal punishment after death with dissection, and licenced physicians could only procure unclaimed dead bodies for study from places such as hospitals, asylums and workhouses. However, given that it was the poor who were most likely to leave their relatives unclaimed, this certainly left those most disadvantaged in life to be further disadvantaged in death. In the United States, a series of anatomy acts, beginning with that in the state of Massachusetts in 1831, had a similar effect to the UK Anatomy Act. However, some Southern states continued to allow the anatomical study of those who died in prison, where a disproportionate number of inmates were African American. Such practices were a terrible stain on the history of anatomy.

▲ *Auschwitz provided cadavers for dissection.*

NAZI ATROCITIES

Between 1933 and 1945, Germany's Third Reich prioritized teaching and research to improve understanding of the human body, for the purpose of extolling the superiority of their 'master' Aryan race over 'inferior' humans, as part of their eugenics movement. For their research, many German anatomists made use of the victims of Hitler's Nazi genocide.

Victims, most of whom were prisoners in concentration camps, included Jews, Sinti, Roma and Eastern Europeans; prisoners of war; those deemed 'sexual deviants', anti-Nazi or criminals; and psychiatric patients. Their bodies were transported to anatomy departments across Germany and its occupied territories, including Poland, Austria and the Czech Republic. The number delivered for dissection is not known, but is estimated to be tens of thousands.

Those who carried out the dissections were not all passive recipients. Although some questioned the morality of the practice, others, like anatomy professors Eduard Pernkopf and August Hirt, were entirely complicit. In 1943, as an SS officer, Hirt ordered the killing of 86 Jews so he could put on a skeleton display at the Anatomy Institute at the Reich University, Strasbourg, to show guests how he believed Jews differed. Although his commands were heeded, the display never came about.

PERNKOPF'S ATLAS

Pernkopf produced one of the most comprehensive and accurate human anatomy textbooks. Published in the 1950s, the *Atlas of Topographical and Applied Human Anatomy* took more than 20 years to complete. This multi-volume map of the human body was the first to use four-colour offset printing, helping anatomists and surgeons worldwide identify structures that looked almost identical to the illustrations. It was not until the late 20th century that investigations revealed that the images in the atlas had made use of the victims of genocide. Some scholars argue for use of the atlas to be discontinued, while others believe the knowledge gained should be used for teaching medical ethics, history and anatomy to honour the victims of the Nazis.

LEARNING FROM THE PAST

Although lessons have been learned, it is vital that we never forget those who were robbed of their human dignity while our knowledge of anatomy was expanded. Anatomical specimens in many museums and collections include those of unknown origin, of which many were obtained without consent. Most serve as a constant and stark reminder of anatomy's shadowy past. Others have been given a fitting burial in commemoration of their non-consensual and immoral sacrifice.

▲ *The anatomist John Hunter is seen with the skeleton (feet) of 'Irish giant' Charles Byrne, displayed against Byrne's express wishes.*

TALKING ANATOMESE

In addition to appreciating key events in the history of anatomy, understanding the language of anatomy will also help boost your comprehension of the field. The terms used to describe the different anatomical structures and their relative positions stem from the different languages spoken by the founding anatomists.

ANATOMICAL PLANES

When a cadaver is divided into sections, the plane at which the cuts are made are as follows:

Median: The cut is made vertically down the middle of the body, through the midline, and produces two equal left and right sections. If the cut is made parallel to the median plane but to either left or right, producing unequal portions, it is called the sagittal plane.

Coronal: The cut is made vertically at right angles to the median plane, producing front and back halves.

Horizontal (or axial or transverse): The cut is made horizontally, at right angles to both the coronal and median planes, producing top and bottom parts.

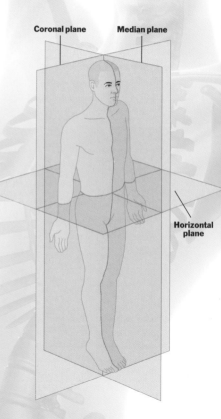

▶ The main anatomical planes are not just used during dissections but also in medical imaging to describe the different sections of the body examined during computed tomography (CT) or magnetic resonance imaging (MRI) scans.

THE ANATOMICAL POSITION

Also known as the standard position, anatomical position refers to the position of your body when you stand erect, facing forward with your arms positioned so that your forearms are supinated (with the palms open, facing forward, and your thumbs pointing away from your body). Your forearms are pronated if your palms face backward and your thumbs point into your body. All terms that describe the position of a structure in your body are given relative to the standard position. It is a reference point that helps medical professionals navigate their way around your body.

TERM	MEANING
Superior	Above another structure
Inferior	Below another structure
Anterior	In front of another structure
Posterior	Behind another structure
Ventral	Toward the front of the body (surfaces)
Dorsal	Toward the back of the body (surfaces)
Medial	Closest to the midline
Lateral	Farthest from the midline
Proximal	Nearest to its origin (or to the trunk)
Distal	Farthest from its origin (or from the trunk)

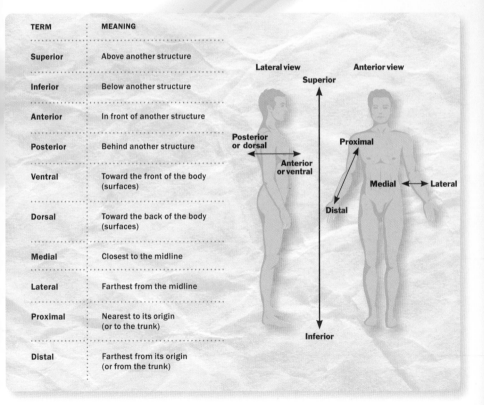

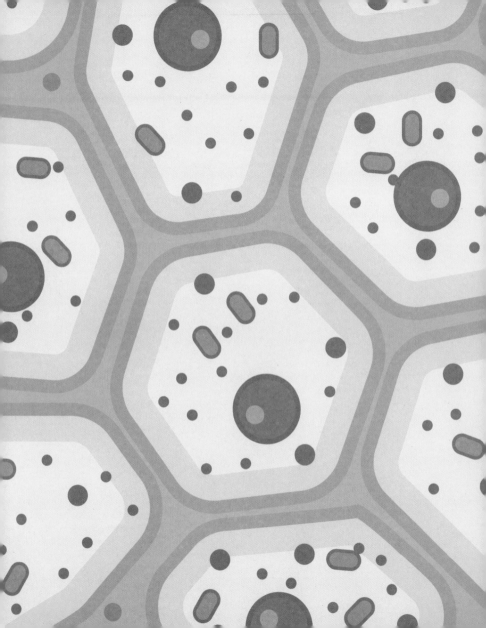

CHAPTER 2

BIT BY BIT

ORGANIZATION OF YOUR BODY

The ancient Greek philosopher and biologist Aristotle said something along the lines of: 'The whole is greater than the sum of its parts.' However, when it comes to the human body, is that true? It is also commonplace to say that the small things matter and the best things come in small packages. When it comes to how you are assembled, one could argue that the whole depends on its parts working together.

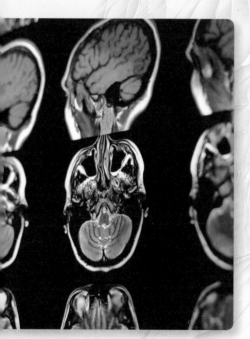

Your body is a live demonstration of what it means to work as a team. It is the quintessential biological institution, because every single member is valued and plays a vital role. Indeed, without any subordinates, the greater structures simply would not exist.

As with any organization, to appreciate fully the different parts and functions of our anatomy, it helps to have a visual chart of where every entity fits in. Cue the hierarchical structure of the human body: an ordered pyramidal system that summarizes the basic architecture of every human, with increasing complexity.

◄ This magnetic resonance imaging (MRI) scan shows the brain. You have several organs that you cannot live without, but your brain is the only one that cannot be replaced.

HIERARCHY OF THE HUMAN BODY

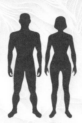

Organism: As a walking–talking medley of 'subservient' biological structures and systems, you are truly at the mercy of your smaller parts.

Organ systems: When organs join forces, the result is the organ system. Organ systems are interconnected networks of distinct anatomical structures whose purpose is to ensure the major functions of the body are met. Some systems are linked, and some are not, but they all communicate with each other.

ORGANISM

ORGAN SYSTEMS

ORGANS

TISSUES

CELLS

ATOMS

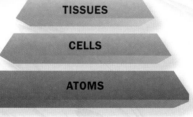

Organs: Organs are recognizable to the naked eye. They are made up of two or more tissue types that work together to conduct a specific physiological function(s).

Tissues: Tissues are made of an army of similar, connected cells with a specific purpose in mind. There are four distinct types of tissue (see pages 44–5).

Cells: These are the smallest unit of an organism that can perform independently all the things we do to survive. Cells can replicate, use or make energy, grow, die, communicate and excrete, although not necessarily in that order.

Atoms: At the most basic level, we are indistinguishable from inanimate objects. Subatomic particles comprise the simplest building blocks of all matter. Around seven quadrillion (7 followed by 15 zeros) protons, electrons and neutrons are said to make up your entire body.

CELL STRUCTURE

The English polymath Robert Hooke (1635–1703) is credited as being the first person to discover the cell. In 1665, he used an early form of microscope to examine slices of cork. He noted that they looked remarkably like small rooms called '*cellula*' that monks inhabited at the time, and so the name 'cell' was born. In truth, what he saw were the dead walls of plant cells, which had a honeycomb-like structure.

INSIDE A TYPICAL CELL

▶ *A single cell is populated with a diverse community of tiny structures, or organelles, that each serve specific functions within the cell.*

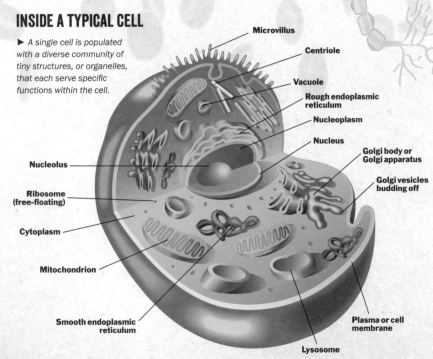

Microvillus

Centriole

Vacuole

Rough endoplasmic reticulum

Nucleoplasm

Nucleus

Golgi body or Golgi apparatus

Golgi vesicles budding off

Nucleolus

Ribosome (free-floating)

Cytoplasm

Mitochondrion

Smooth endoplasmic reticulum

Plasma or cell membrane

Lysosome

BIGGEST AND SMALLEST

Of the 200 or so different types of cells in your body, the largest and smallest are those responsible for your very existence. Measuring 0.5mm (⅕₀in) in diameter, the female egg is just about visible to the naked eye. Contrast that with a sperm cell, which can only be seen with a microscope. Its 'head' is about 0.004mm (¹/₆₂₅₀in) long.

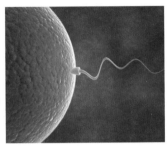

Over the centuries, different parts of the cell have been discovered by a wealth of scientific talent. In the 19th century, German scientists Theodor Schwann, Matthias Jakob Schleiden and Rudolf Virchow helped formulate cell theory. One of its tenets provides the perfect starting point: it stipulates that the cell is the basic unit of life.

There are trillions of cells in your body. What they do is often governed by what they look like (and vice versa). However, there are fundamental structural similarities. Irrespective of cell type, all cells are filled with a watery jelly-like matrix that is encased by an outer cell membrane which controls what comes in and what goes out. This matrix, or cytoplasm, helps the cell maintain its structure. It also suspends microscopic organs of life, called organelles, which help cells carry out their specific duties. At this point, differences start to appear based on which organelles are present and in what amount.

NUCLEUS

All your cells possess (or start off having) a control centre called a nucleus. This chief of organelles determines to which phylum you belong: whether you are a simple organism, like a bacterium, that lacks a nucleus, or a more complex organism, which has one. As the brain of the cell, the nucleus occupies central position and houses a very special code, your genetic information, in the form of deoxyribonucleic acid (DNA). The fact that the nucleus has its very own special matrix plus a 'double' membrane is testament to its high ranking within the cell.

Mitochondrion

Endoplasmic reticulum

MITOCHONDRION

If there were one organelle that could rightly contest the nucleus for its crown status it would be a sausage-shaped structure called the mitochondrion. Not only do mitochondria bear the hallmarks of an evolutionary giant, with their double membrane and own genetic system, but they determine whether a cell lives or dies. It is said that mitochondria evolved from bacteria that once invaded the cell. These biological squatters only managed to secure their tenancy by establishing a symbiotic relationship with their cellular landlord.

Comparable to electric generators, mitochondria produce all the energy that a cell needs to conduct its business. Without their power, organelles would serve as mere floating bits of detritus. Mitochondria use oxygen to help convert the energy stored in nutrients such

as glucose into high-energy molecules called adenosine triphosphate (ATP), which drive all the chemical reactions in the cell. This process, known as aerobic cellular respiration, also produces carbon dioxide, water and heat. Cells need their ATP fuel because they are in the business of making proteins (see pages 34–5).

ENDOPLASMIC RETICULUM AND RIBOSOMES

With instructions from the nucleus, the protein data is dispatched to several organelles in a cascading fashion. First are the ribosomes, which can be found either floating freely in the cytoplasm or bound to a membranous network of canals called the endoplasmic reticulum (ER). The spherical ribosomes receive the template upon which a protein is built.

The ER operates in a conveyor-belt like manner and receives the proteins

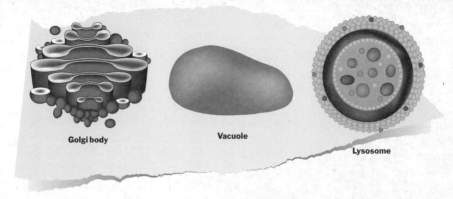

Golgi body

Vacuole

Lysosome

assembled by the attached ribosomes. These flat, folded membranes help products from the nucleus reach deep into the cytoplasm, enabling the internal transport and export of proteins such as antibodies (for use by the immune system) and enzymes (which bring about chemical reactions). Not all ER have ribosomes attached. Those without are known as smooth ER and manufacture components of fats, as well as hormones and chemical ions that trigger reactions.

GOLGI BODY

It would be remiss not to acknowledge how these cell products are packaged and bundled for use within and outside the cell. Named after the Italian biologist Camillo Golgi (1843–1926), stacks of membranes called a Golgi body, or Golgi apparatus, provide a shuttle service

and add the final touches to the ER proteins before packing them into small membrane-bound vesicles.

VACUOLE

Large, fluid-filled vesicles called vacuoles act as floating storage units for a variety of substances that are either needed by the cell, such as nutrients and enzymes, or deliberately quarantined.

LYSOSOME

With all these activities going on, the cell would be hard pushed not to make any mess. Luckily, each cell has its own recycling centre in the form of lysosomes. Except, you would not want to go inside one because it is packed with enzymes that digest and reprocess worn out components of the cell, as well as target invading foreign bodies and the cell itself, if it is damaged beyond repair.

◀ Nobel Prize-winning duo James Watson (left) and Francis Crick (right) deduced the molecular structure of DNA based on work conducted by X-ray crystallographers Maurice Wilkins and Rosalind Franklin.

DNA: IT'S ALL ABOUT THE BASE(S)

Cells make proteins, and the blueprint for them comes directly from your genes housed in the nucleus. These organized sequences of biological data, inherited from your parents, affect all aspects of how your body works. From your physical appearance to how you digest food, the coded instructions in these basic units of heredity all boil down to one extraordinary molecule: DNA.

It would be sacrilegious to describe the structure of DNA and not mention James Watson (born 1928) and Francis Crick (1916–2004). In 1953, these Cambridge dons identified the molecular structure of DNA. Put in the simplest terms, the structure is like a bendy ladder cut vertically into two equal parts. Broadly, each side, or rail, of the ladder is made of two consecutively arranged compounds: a phosphate group and a sugar molecule

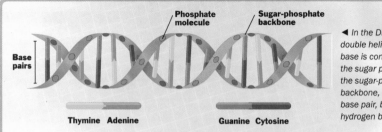

Base pairs

Phosphate molecule

Sugar-phosphate backbone

Thymine   Adenine   Guanine   Cytosine

◄ In the DNA double helix, each base is connected to the sugar portion of the sugar-phosphate backbone, and to its base pair, by weak hydrogen bonds.

known as deoxyribose. That is DNA's backbone. Attached at 90 degrees to the rail (at each sugar insert) is an organic (carbon-based) molecule known as a base, which forms half of the rung. These bases are of different types: A (adenine), C (cytosine), G (guanine) and T (thymine). Their arrangement holds the key to the genetic code.

If we bring both rails back together and use weak hydrogen bonds to join the bases jutting out of either side, this will form loosely held rungs, or base pairs. (Basically, a hydrogen bond is a special type of attraction or force between a hydrogen atom and another atom.) These bases must be matched with the right (complimentary) bases on the opposite side to ensure a good fit. In a DNA molecule, A links with T only, and G with C. The ladder is then twisted into a helical shape – and voilà, you have DNA.

WHY THE TWIST?

It is humbling to think we owe everything to a daisy chain of molecules arranged like swirly marshmallow tubes. But do not be fooled. Behind this formation lies an ingenious advantage. It is claimed that the twist protects the bases from toxic interactions and supports the supercoiling of DNA into tightly packed chromosomes (see pages 36–7) so it can fit its 6 billion base pairs into a single cell. More than likely, however, given that DNA's bases cannot tolerate water and your cells are full of it, a twisted structure confers maximum shielding for the most cosseted inner region.

MAKING PROTEINS

Proteins are long molecules made of chains of one or more amino acids, in an order laid down by the base sequence in the relevant portion of DNA. Proteins are essential for the structure and functioning of all the body's cells, tissues and organs. How does DNA go from a double helix to making proteins? The missing link is ribonucleic acid (RNA).

DNA and RNA look very much alike, except RNA is a single strand and its sugar component is made of ribose (it is not a 'deoxy' because, unlike DNA, it is not missing an oxygen atom). Unlike DNA, RNA does not pair adenine (A) with the base thymine (T): it matches adenine with a base called uracil (U). The theory is that, during its evolution, DNA traded its uracil for thymine because it makes for a structure that is steadier and more resilient to entities in the cell that could destroy it. Clearly, this makes for a much safer way to store genetic information in the long term.

TRANSCRIPTION

When a gene is switched on to make a protein, or 'expressed', the exact portion of DNA that codes for that specific gene unwinds and surreptitiously unzips itself. In doing so, it flashes its raw bases to a protein called RNA polymerase. This enzyme transcribes the code along one DNA strand by adding successive building blocks together comprising a phosphate group, a ribose sugar and an attached base – collectively referred to as a ribonucleotide – all the while ensuring that the bases adhere to the GC and AU pairing rule. This results in the formation of an RNA molecule called messenger RNA (mRNA), in a process known as transcription.

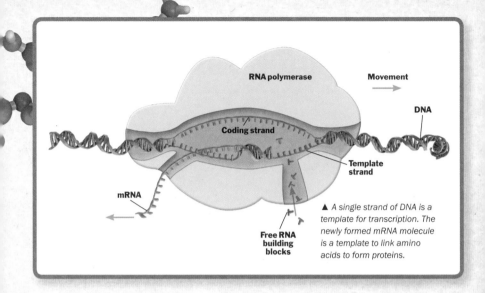

▲ A single strand of DNA is a template for transcription. The newly formed mRNA molecule is a template to link amino acids to form proteins.

Evidently, it is far safer for copies of the code to be shunting around the cell than the hallowed DNA itself. Once completed, mRNA trundles out of the nucleus through its membrane pore and enters the cytoplasm, where it engages with ribosomes to continue the process of translating the code into amino acids.

NEW PROTEINS

New proteins are earmarked for internal use or export outside the cell. Enzymes are among those used internally and exported: these speed up chemical reactions. Proteins that stay within the cell include receptors that embed themselves in the outer membrane. They convert outside signals into actions within the cell. Membrane proteins can also be traffic lights, controlling passage of molecules across the cell membrane.

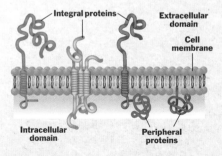

▶ Membrane proteins intrinsic to the cell membrane are called integral proteins. They have different functions depending on their structure.

COILING INTO CHROMOSOMES

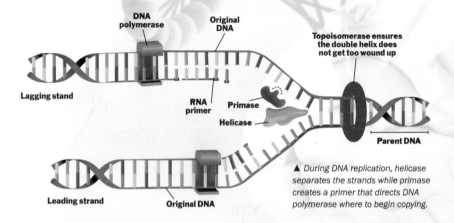

DNA polymerase

Original DNA

Topoisomerase ensures the double helix does not get too wound up

Lagging stand

RNA primer

Primase

Helicase

Parent DNA

Leading strand

Original DNA

▲ During DNA replication, helicase separates the strands while primase creates a primer that directs DNA polymerase where to begin copying.

Chromosomes are DNA that is tightly coiled around spool-like proteins called histones. Each of your cells (other than your reproductive cells) contains 23 pairs of chromosomes, or 46 in total, which is referred to as the diploid number of chromosomes. One set came from your mother and the other from your father. DNA only coils neatly into chromosomes when the cell is getting ready to divide. It is only at this point that chromosomes become visible under a microscope. If DNA did not form into chromosomes, it would become a horrible tangle during cell division.

Before a cell can divide, it must first replicate its DNA. This requires that the DNA strands unzip themselves to aid replication. The aim is to create two copies of the same genetic material, so one can be passed down from the 'parent' cell to its new daughter cells. The enzyme DNA polymerase directs the process, helped by other proteins: for example, DNA helicase unzips the helix.

It is vital these new 'complimentary' strands of DNA are copied correctly. So, a proofreading exercise ensues before the new DNA twists into a double helix. The new DNA strand is a hybrid: half new strand and half the template strand, which provides for a more accurate result than if the two entirely new strands joined.

CHROMOSOME SHAPE

The two copies of DNA (referred to as sister chromatids) condense and glue together at a corset-like constriction point called a centromere. This divides the chromosome into two sections, or arms. Each chromosome corresponds to a different double helix with its own set of linked genes.

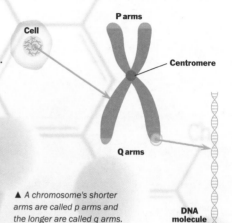

▲ A chromosome's shorter arms are called p arms and the longer are called q arms.

CHROMOSOME PAIRS

Your DNA codes for 20,000 to 25,000 genes, each providing instructions for making proteins. Your complete set of genes, or genome, is divided across 23 pairs of chromosomes, but not equally. Chromosome pair 1 is the largest, holding about 2,100 genes. Let's compare this with the last pair, chromosome 23, which determines your sex. One of these sex chromosomes – the biggest of this pair – is called the X chromosome; the smaller is called Y. (These terms have nothing to do with the chromosome shapes.) Those who inherit two copies of the X chromosome develop into females. Those that get an X and Y become males. In men, chromosome Y, inherited from their father, is shorter than chromosome X, inherited from their mother, because it contains only 50 to 70 rather than 800 genes.

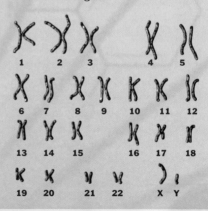

DIVIDING CELLS

Cells must divide in order to replace lost or damaged cells. They must also divide to allow for growth and to create germ cells that unite and transform you from a fertilized egg into an adult. Cell division is a complicated affair and must be strictly regulated. Failure to do so can be catastrophic not just for your cell but your very survival.

Depending on the messages a cell receives, it either continues resting, quietly carrying out its everyday activities, or enters active division. The portion of the cell cycle that leads up to division is called interphase.

During this stage, a cell increases in size, doubles up its organelles, replicates its DNA and prepares for division. Then, depending on the type of cell, it will divide either by mitosis or meiosis.

MITOSIS

Mitosis produces two identical daughter cells, each containing the same diploid number of chromosomes as the original parent cell. The cell divides only once, but the chromosomes perform an intricate four-step dance.

Prophase: In the opening sequence of division, named prophase, the nuclear membrane dissolves and the sister chromatids condense and join at the centromere before pairing up with their counterparts inherited from the other parent.

Metaphase: Next, all the chromosomes converge in the centre, assisted by rope-like proteins called microtubules, which attach either side of each chromosome's centromere. The microtubules are themselves attached to a winch-like structure called a centrosome, which organizes them.

MEIOSIS

Sexual reproduction relies upon a type of cell division called meiosis, which produces sperm and egg cells. Meiosis produces four non-identical daughter cells, each containing half the number of chromosomes as the original parent (called a haploid number of chromosomes). This arises because the cell divides twice. Unlike in mitosis, the daughter cells are genetically different from their parent cell and each other.

▶ *Prior to meiosis 1, the sperm cell goes through interphase. It then enters the first step, prophase 1, where genetic material is exchanged among homologous chromosome pairs. For eggs, completion of meiosis 2 occurs at fertilization.*

Sperm parent cell

Prophase 1

Meiosis 1

Meiosis 2

Daughter cells

Anaphase: The centrosome leads the next movement, anaphase, which sees the sister chromatids be pulled apart to opposite ends of the cell.

Telophase: The nuclear membrane reforms around the now solitary chromatids and the cytoplasm divides in two.

Cytokinesis: During cytokinesis, the cell fully divides in two, re-sheathed within the cell membrane.

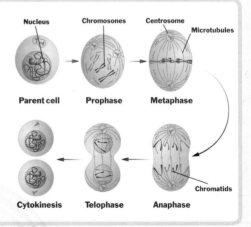

Nucleus · Chromosones · Centrosome · Microtubules

Parent cell · Prophase · Metaphase

Cytokinesis · Telophase · Anaphase · Chromatids

CELL DIVERSITY

Your cells work, doing a job for their boss – you. Having a diverse workforce in terms of background, expertise, and role leads to a more robust and dynamic organization. That is why you are not a giant amoeba or a plank of uniform cells. At the last roll call, you employ around 206 different types of cells who do your bidding in their own specialized way. Let's introduce you to a few of them.

PHOTORECEPTORS

Photoreceptors are cells that reside in the retina at the back of your eye. They contain light-sensitive pigments that allow them to respond to the incoming light to help you see. These cells are uniquely designed to convert the image entering your eye into a nerve signal that your brain interprets as a picture. Two types of photoreceptor are deployed.

Rods help you perceive light, dark and movement, while cones bring you the colour.

RED BLOOD CELLS

To secure what is possibly the most crucial role a cell can have, red blood cells (RBCs) made the ultimate contract of waiving their nucleus in exchange for more work space. This structural

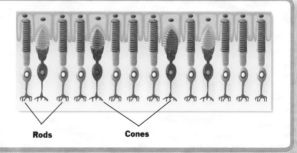

▶ Rods and cones populate outer layers of a thin tissue of specialized cells called the retina. Rods are more abundant, particularly at the retinal edges. Cones are more prominent in the retinal centre.

Rods   **Cones**

modification, which makes them unlike any other cell in your body, permits them to carry as much oxygen as possible and deliver this life-sustaining gas to your tissues. This is such an important job that RBCs account for almost a third of the entire population of cells found in your body.

HORMONE AND ENZYME MAKERS

Cells located in your endocrine and digestive systems have additional tools to fulfil their duties. These cells contain extra ribosomes and Golgi bodies to produce and package the hormones and digestive enzymes they secrete into your blood or stomach respectively.

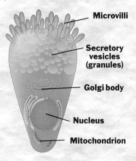

▼ Goblet cells are found along your intestines and airways. They have lots of secretory vesicles that form the protective substance mucus.

- Microvilli
- Secretory vesicles (granules)
- Golgi body
- Nucleus
- Mitochondrion

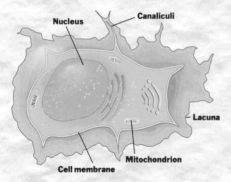

Nucleus
Canaliculi
Lacuna
Mitochondrion
Cell membrane

▲ An osteocyte occupies a space in bone known as a lacuna. It has many processes (extensions of the cytoplasm) that connect with other osteocytes through tiny canals called canaliculi.

BONE CELLS

The hardest cells in your body are in the bone department, which is constantly changing and reforming. This job is delegated to three cells. Osteoblasts produce the matrix that makes bone, and some mature into cells called osteocytes that literally get stuck in the product of their own making. Osteocytes are the most common type of bone cell and make up most of your bone, which they help to co-ordinate and reshape, especially when it is stressed. Osteoclasts reabsorb bone material either to release essential minerals locked in the matrix, such as calcium, or following periods of inactivity.

STEM CELLS

There is a very special type of cell that is exalted because of its latent regenerative abilities. Stem cells have the potential to self-renew and produce any type of cell in your body. These cells can be found patiently waiting to be activated in several tissues and organs.

Unlike most cells, stem cells are undifferentiated, which means they are not specialized and do not have any specific roles or defined features, unlike the cells discussed on the previous pages. Once given the green light to divide, a stem cell's progeny includes a cell that remains undifferentiated and another destined for specialization.

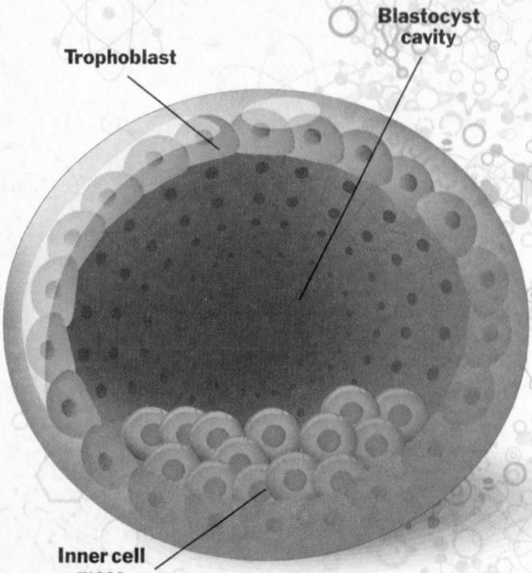

EMBRYONIC STEM CELLS

There are two main types of stem cells, depending on their source of origin. Embryonic stem cells are found only in very young embryos called blastocysts. These cells have the natural ability to become absolutely any cell in your body and for this reason are known as being 'pluri'-potent.

Blastocyst cavity

Trophoblast

Inner cell mass

◀ Embryonic stem cells are derived from the inner cell mass of a blastocyst, the region that develops into the fetus. The trophoblast develops into the placenta.

ADULT STEM CELLS

Adult stem cells are found in most adult tissues. Until recently, they were thought only to give rise to a limited number of different cell types related to their tissue of origin. However, research suggests that these 'multi'-potent adult stem cells are not as restricted as initially thought. Indeed, researchers are now able to manipulate them chemically to grow into various types of cells that originate from different tissues. Furthermore, scientists have successfully managed to reprogram or induce 'regular' (or non-stem) adult cells that have already specialized or differentiated to have pluri-potent stem cell properties.

The transformative potential of these advances in regenerative medicine is vast. Not only would it circumvent the ethical dilemma of using human embryos to harvest pluri-potent cells, it also provides a potential panacea to the problem of transplanted material being rejected by the immune system.

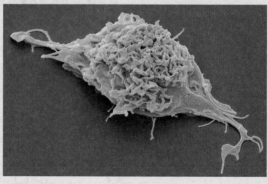

▶ This coloured scanning electron micrograph (SEM) shows a stem cell from bone marrow. Also known as somatic stem cells, adult stem cells are found in children and adults.

THE TISSUE QUARTET

As a fetus, your cells were forced along specific paths of differentiation to form a quartet of distinct tissue types. These evolved when those specialized cells discovered their kind and joined together to form well-defined colonies. Epithelial, connective, muscular and neural are the four types of tissue.

EPITHELIAL

Epithelial tissue crops up in your border areas, such as your skin, the lining of your digestive system, and your eyes. It also lines the surfaces of your internal organs and respiratory tract, your nose, mouth and lungs. This tissue exists in many different forms, from a single layer of flat or cuboidal cells to complex multilayered varieties.

▼ The epithelial cells (stained red) that line the folds of the intestinal wall are called the mucosal membrane or mucosa.

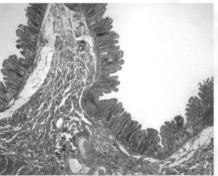

Epithelial cells form a barrier between your organs and invading substances and microorganisms. They rely on a single sheet of cells, the basement membrane, which anchors the epithelium to the rest of your body and helps to regulate what passes through. Modified epithelial tissue includes glands that secrete substances, allowing your nose to secrete mucus, your stomach to produce digestive enzymes, and your skin to secrete sweat and sebum.

CONNECTIVE

If stem cells are multi-potent with regard to the different cells they can become, then connective tissue cells should be called 'ubiqui'-potent, because they are everywhere. Connective tissue is the single most common tissue type found in your body. These cells make your bone tissue, cartilage, tendons, ligaments, fat tissue, and even your blood since they have the same embryonic origin (the embryo's mesoderm, or middle layer of cells). As their name implies, connective tissue cells serve to connect the different parts of your body. They do this by producing a matrix that varies in consistency (from fluid to fibrous or solid) and embeds the cells that produce it. This supportive tissue helps bind different tissues within an organ and cushions the delicate ones, stores energy and provides structural support.

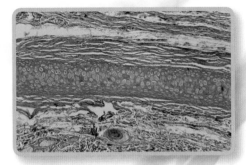

▲ This micrograph shows a band of cartilage tissue (stained blue). Cartilage is a flexible type of connective tissue found in various places throughout the body.

MUSCULAR

The cellular component of muscular tissue is the myofibre, so called because of the long shape of these cells. Their nucleus is spread across the edge of the cell membrane to allow more space for the thousands of myofilaments packed inside. Myofilaments allow muscle contraction because, like interlocking fingers, they overlap and slide across each other, making the cell shorter. For more on muscle structure, see pages 98–9.

NEURAL

Neural tissue is the main tissue of the nervous system. It serves to generate and conduct electrical impulses that lead to movement and/or secretion of bodily fluids. The main component of neural tissue is the neuron, or nerve cell, which communicates with other cells through connections called synapses. The neurons are provided with nutrients, and their nerve impulses are helped along, by glial cells. For more on nerve cells, see pages 190–91.

COUNTING OUR ORGANS

You have either 78 or 79 different organs. Part of this uncertainty arises from the lack of a universally accepted standard definition of what an organ is. What is clear, is that organs comprise a mixture of tissues working harmoniously together to achieve specific body objectives.

When most people think organ, they think of the five vital organs: the brain, heart, kidney, liver and lungs. However, in the urinary system alone, there are a further three organs in addition to the kidney: the bladder, ureter and urethra. Of your internal organs (or viscera), the liver is the biggest and weighs 1.8kg (4lb) in an average man. However, weighing about 2.7kg (6lb) is your skin, which wins the organ heavyweight title.

Worthy of its own championship title is your brain, as it is the most energy-consuming organ, taking 20 per cent of what you produce. It also houses your smallest organ, the pineal gland, which churns out the hormone melatonin to help you sleep.

ORGAN SYSTEMS

The classification of your organ systems is no better when it comes to nailing down the actual number you have. This book will introduce you to 10 organ systems:

- Integumentary
- Musculoskeletal
- Cardiovascular
- Lymphatic
- Respiratory
- Nervous
- Endocrine
- Digestive
- Urinary
- Reproductive

However, some experts consider the immune system separate from the lymphatic, and the muscular system separate to the skeletal. Others place the immune and lymphatic systems together with the cardiovascular system to form the circulatory system. Irrespective of these system-swapping shenanigans, what is important to note is that your organ systems do not work in isolation: there are considerable overlaps that render an exact classification somewhat immaterial.

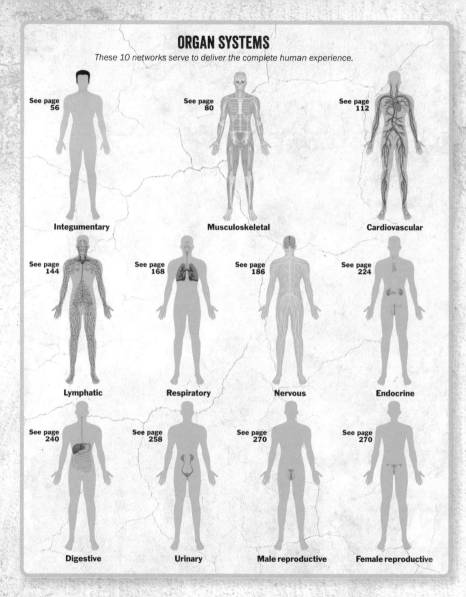

ORGAN SYSTEMS

These 10 networks serve to deliver the complete human experience.

See page 56

Integumentary

See page 80

Musculoskeletal

See page 112

Cardiovascular

See page 144

Lymphatic

See page 168

Respiratory

See page 186

Nervous

See page 224

Endocrine

See page 240

Digestive

See page 258

Urinary

See page 270

Male reproductive

See page 270

Female reproductive

BALANCING THE BODY

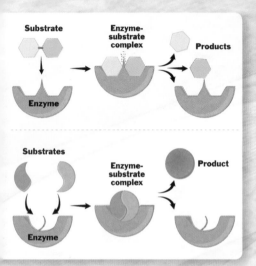

Substrate — Enzyme-substrate complex — Products

Enzyme

Substrates — Enzyme-substrate complex — Product

Enzyme

Your organ systems support the maintenance of two connected body-wide processes: metabolism and homeostasis. Metabolism is not just about how fast you burn food to produce energy. It represents the sum total of all the different chemical reactions occurring in your body. Homeostasis is the way your body seeks to achieve internal balance regardless of conditions.

◀ The active site of an enzyme has a unique shape (akin to a lock). The reaction will only proceed once the right substrate (key) fits. The products may either be degraded or combined.

METABOLISM

Metabolism is about more than just breaking down the food you eat into its component parts – protein, carbohydrates and sugars – in a process called catabolism. Metabolism also includes the reverse process, known as anabolism, which describes how your body uses smaller molecules, such as amino acids or fatty acids, to build more complex molecules that can be stored as energy or used for things from growth to fighting infections. The speed at which all this occurs depends on factors such as your age, gender and genetics.

Enzymes are sometimes considered to be the effectors of metabolism. This is because they are biological catalysts, helping speed up chemical reactions in a cell. These ball-shaped proteins are mandated to catalyze reactions by virtue of their structure. They contain a gap, or active site, which allows molecules that fit (called their 'substrates') to lock into them, where they are either broken into two smaller parts (degraded) or combined to build a larger molecule.

It is quite easy to recognize an enzyme by name alone: the suffix '-ase' denotes an enzyme (for example, polymerase, amylase, and dehydrogenase). Most enzymes are contained within a cell. Their presence in the blood can indicate potential tissue damage. For example, lactate dehydrogenase (LDH) is normally present in liver and heart cells, so raised levels in the blood suggest possible damage to these organs.

The amount of enzymes produced is tightly regulated to avoid any reaction occurring either too quickly or too slowly, which would otherwise alter the balance of substances in the body and ultimately affect homeostasis.

HOMEOSTASIS

Homeostasis is a dynamic and automatic process that aims to achieve inner physiological peace. Homeostasis relies heavily on getting feedback from different organ systems, in particular from your nervous and endocrine systems. Through a series of negative feedback loops your body is able to coordinate responses and minimize any imbalances, because failure to do so can lead to disease and, at worst, death.

HOMEOSTASIS IN ACTION

Several organ systems are used to help regulate the volume of water in the body. When the body is dehydrated, the amount of water in the blood falls. This causes a structure in your brain called the hypothalamus to register the change, a signal you interpret as thirst. The hypothalamus also secretes hormones that make your kidneys conserve water. You drink water until the levels in the blood are replenished. The hypothalamus registers this new change and subsequently decreases the levels of hormones it sends to the kidneys.

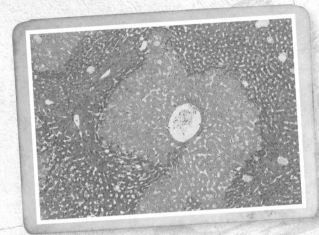

◄ Lack of oxygen or nutrients (or exposure to toxic agents) can cause liver cells to die by necrosis. Note their paler cytoplasm and loss of a nucleus, tissue architecture and the presence of inflammatory cells (black dots).

WHEN CELLS DIE

A basic feature of all living things, whether they are uni- or multicellular, is the guarantee that they will die. This rather paradoxical trait used to define the very characteristics of being alive reinforces the notion that with life comes death. At the cellular level, death is a remarkable event. The signalling pathways that orchestrate this sovereign of all tasks are as diverse and complex as life itself.

From a unicellular perspective, cell death is a fate that ends life. However, for all multicellular organisms (metazoans), cell death has been known since the turn of the 20th century to play a significant part in normal development processes. Historically, cell death (in a mature organism) was regarded more as an enemy of life, analogous to the running down of a clockwork mechanism, any noxious exposures accelerating this demise. Such a view no longer holds true, owing to the realization that many forms of injury caused by external agents may trigger a suicide program and thus provide a mechanism for disposing

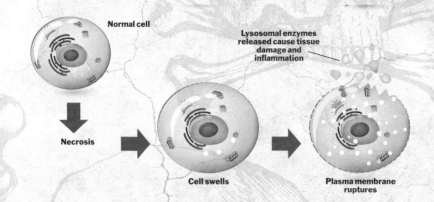

Normal cell

Lysosomal enzymes released cause tissue damage and inflammation

Necrosis

Cell swells

Plasma membrane ruptures

▲ *During necrosis, cells lose their ability to regulate the transport of substances in and out of the cell. The cell and organelles swell and rupture, releasing their contents into the extracellular fluid.*

of damaged cells – a hugely desirable adaptation.

Since the 1990s, scientists have overseen an explosion in their understanding of the mechanisms involved in cell death, of which two distinct modes have been identified: accidental and programmed.

ACCIDENTAL CELL DEATH: NECROSIS

Accidental cell death arises unexpectedly, with no purpose in mind, and is considered detrimental to the organism as a whole. Accidental cell death is sometimes referred to as 'pathological cell death' or, more specifically, 'necrosis' (derived from the Greek word 'nekroo', meaning kill). Cells that undergo such a fate are almost always the victims of severe and acute injury, caused by:

- Extreme changes in a cell's electrolyte–water balance (electrolytes are salts and minerals)
- Sudden and prolonged shortage of nutrients
- Abrupt lack of oxygen (anoxia)
- Extreme physical and chemical injuries caused by intense exposure to heat, toxic chemicals or pressure

Necrosis is used to describe the changes that cells and tissues undergo following accidental cell death. Cells and organelles are unable to control their volume and swell up, eventually rupturing and spilling their contents into the surrounding area. This is very messy and also triggers an inflammatory response in the local area.

PROGRAMMED CELL DEATH: APOPTOSIS

In stark contrast, programmed cell death (PCD) represents the scheduled or controlled instruction to die. PCD is a tightly regulated procedure within the development plan of an organism. This natural or 'physiological' form of cell death, occurs in particular tissues at specific times during development, or during all life stages, as during the renewal of immune cells. The removal of unwanted and potentially dangerous cells is dependent on PCD. In accordance with this, PCD can be induced by a variety of stimuli, but is executed by a process called apoptosis.

The word apoptosis (from the Greek for the 'falling off' of leaves from trees) was coined by pathologist Andrew Wyllie and colleagues in 1971. Apoptosis is an intrinsic death program inside cells which, when implemented, provides a clean and efficient way of removing unwanted and dying cells. Although the terms PCD and apoptosis are often used synonymously, there are

instances when PCD is not apoptosis. For example, the cells that line the womb are programmed to die by the time a woman has her period, but they actually die by necrosis due to a lack of blood supply.

In contrast to necrosis, cells undergoing apoptosis are acted on by a set of proteins called caspases. Furthermore, the cells do not swell but shrink and eventually fragment into membrane-bound vesicles (apoptotic bodies) whose surfaces display markers that attract white blood cells called phagocytes that gobble them up. Unlike during necrosis, leakage of potentially harmful material is prevented by wrapping the cellular components in a protective protein shell.

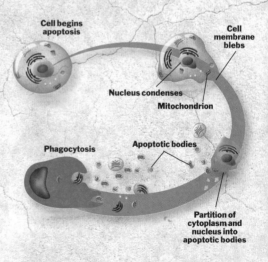

Cell begins apoptosis

Cell membrane blebs

Nucleus condenses

Mitochondrion

Phagocytosis

Apoptotic bodies

Partition of cytoplasm and nucleus into apoptotic bodies

▶ *This illustration shows the key stages of apoptosis. Mitochondria are preserved until later stages, which indicates that apoptosis is a very energy-dependent process.*

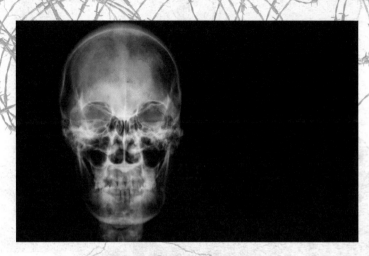

THE DARK SIDE OF APOPTOSIS

Although apoptosis is associated with maintaining normal tissue balance, it is also responsible for a range of human diseases. Consequently, as with necrosis, there is a dark side to apoptosis.

Too little apoptosis (in a cell with an abnormal resistance to apoptosis) results in:

Birth defects: Surplus cells fail to die.

Autoimmune disease: Autoimmune reactive cells persist.

Cancer: Cells with damaged genes that control growth are unable to die and continue to grow.

Too much apoptosis (when apoptosis is activated in a cell when it should not be) results in:

Acquired immune deficiency syndrome (AIDS): White blood cells called T cells die after infection with the human immunodeficiency virus (HIV). For more information, see page 163.

Neurodegenerative diseases: Neurons die, leading to brain impairment. For more on neurons, see pages 190–91.

Stroke: Temporary lack of oxygen to the brain cells causes them to die by apoptosis.

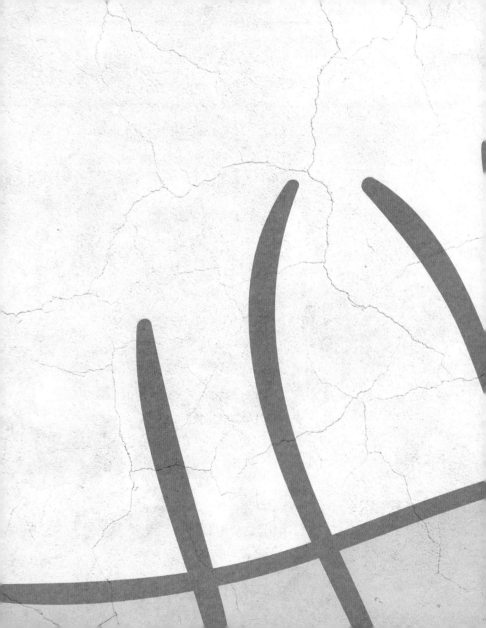

CHAPTER 3

THE ULTIMATE PACKAGING MATERIAL

THE INTEGUMENTARY SYSTEM

A well-known skincare company tells us to 'Love the skin you're in.' You really should, because it is the only one you have. Well, in truth, you do make a brand-new one every month or so, but that's only the top layer...

Your skin is part of the integumentary system. Your skin and its appendages form the integument, a term derived from the Latin word '*integumentum*', meaning 'a covering'. Skin does not just cover the surface of your body but extends into your oral cavity and anal canal. Reasons to love it? Here they are:

- It is the most visible part of your body and influences your looks.
- It comes in a variety of colours.
- It is the main boundary between you and the outside world, forming your first line of defence against harmful chemicals and microbes.
- It helps to control your body temperature.
- It produces a vital bone tonic, vitamin D, when kissed by the sun.
- It is supple yet tough, waterproof and stops you drying out.

▲ Looking after your skin is the least you can do, given what it does for you.

- It provides sensory information about your environment.
- It helps protect you from ultraviolet radiation.

So, what's not to love? Skin certainly deserves some affection. Unlike most coverings that seal their contents, your skin is a very active and versatile, breathing, secretory organ. Plus, it is extremely fussy about what it lets in. If you are, for example, a fat-soluble chemical and desperate to enter the body club, it is best to avoid the soles of the feet as you will be waiting a long time.

THE INTEGUMENT

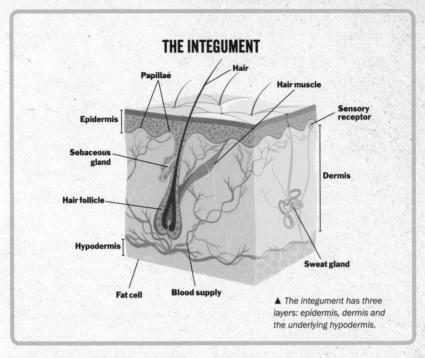

Papillae

Hair

Hair muscle

Sensory receptor

Epidermis

Sebaceous gland

Dermis

Hair follicle

Hypodermis

Sweat gland

Fat cell

Blood supply

▲ The integument has three layers: epidermis, dermis and the underlying hypodermis.

However, the fastest moving queue is on a man's scrotum, so if you want to get in quick that is the place to be.

LAYERS OF THE INTEGUMENT

There are three layers of tissue to contend with. The outer layer, or epidermis, is firmly fixed to the next layer, called the dermis, which is where tattoos get ingrained. Beneath these layers of skin is the hypodermis, mostly made of fat and connecting your skin to your underlying muscle and bone.

Accessory structures of the skin include your hair and nails, as well as glands that secrete either sweat or an oily substance called sebum. They all derive from a layer in an embryo that develops into the epidermis, but extend into the dermis.

If your skin gets damaged, the severity and consequences depend on the number of layers affected, the deeper the more serious. Luckily, your skin is one of the most regenerative parts of your body. For more on its healing abilities, see pages 158–61.

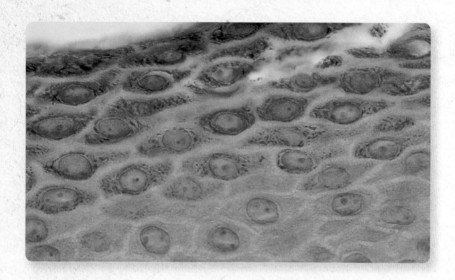

EPIDERMIS

▲ *This micrograph shows the cells of the epidermis. Cells in all the layers above the deepest, basal layer are known as keratinocytes. These gradually die, flatten and harden as new cells underneath push them further up.*

You would be forgiven for assuming the epidermis is structurally nothing more than the top layer of your skin. However, if you delve a bit deeper, you will find that there are layers within this external layer – up to five to be exact.

The lowest layer in the epidermis is the basal layer, which sits just above the dermis and is made up of a single sheet of 'living' epithelial cells (see page 44) called keratinocytes. Unlike the basal layer, the rest of the epidermis is made up of cells that are literally on their way out. Indeed, the epidermis is a place where the dead rest above the living.

Often called the germinal layer, these basal keratinocytes are constantly dividing, producing new cells that are pushed upward. During their ascent, they begin to produce a protein called keratin, which gives the epidermis its tough, waterproof qualities. As the cells ascend higher, they flatten, lose their nucleus, harden and die, leaving the uppermost layer bereft of living cells. This top layer, the stratified corneum, is lost during everyday wear and tear. It is important that the rate of renewal in the basal layer is synchronized with the rate of cell loss in the cornified layer. Imbalance could result in conditions such as psoriasis, where cells are replaced too soon, every 3 to 7 days, and build up into thickened, scale-like plaques.

DESIGNED TO PROTECT

The thickness of your skin varies across your body and is determined by the number of layers in the epidermis and the different levels of stress it must tolerate. The thinnest area is your eyelid, while the thickest is the soles of your feet and palms of your hands, which have five instead of the usual four epidermal layers. The epidermis also bears immune cells called Langerhans cells that scour the skin for invading micro-organisms.

BASEMENT MEMBRANE

The epidermis is cemented to the next layer, the dermis, via a matrix called the basement membrane. Aside from an adhesive role, this membrane protects the lower structures of your skin from potentially damaging entities, including your own cells that may have mutated and become cancerous.

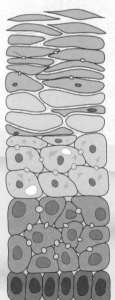

Stratified corneum: Dead cells flake away from this surface layer day by day.

Lucid layer: Aka stratum lucidum, this is present only in the soles of your feet and palms.

Granular layer: Aka stratum granulosum, cells here have more keratin proteins that accumulate as granules.

Spinous layer: Aka stratum spinosum, this layer also includes many Langerhans immune cells.

Basal layer: Aka stratum basale, this layer also contains melanocytes.

▶ *Keratinocytes in the lower layers of the epidermis stick to each other at junctions called desmosomes, which increases the mechanical strength of your skin.*

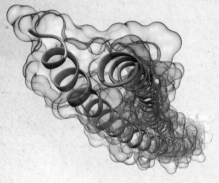
► *This model shows the molecular structure of the protein keratin, which is present in your epidermis, hair and nails.*

MELANOCYTES

One skin cell population particularly at risk of turning malignant are specialized cells called melanocytes. These cells are dotted around the basal layer and produce the dark pigment melanin that colours your skin, hair and iris of your eyes. Melanin does this through finger-like extensions of its cytoplasm called dendrites. Dendrites are also found in nerve cells. In fact, melanocytes and the cells of your nervous system are related, for once upon a time, while you were still a developing embryo, a group of cells destined to become melanocytes pinched off from the same region that developed into your spinal cord.

Like altruistic octopuses, melanocytes pack the melanin into granules called melanosomes and distribute these to neighboring keratinocytes, which absorb them. Once inside, the melanosomes break up and the cells become melanized. This cellular gift-giving act is replicated across your skin and provides it with ultraviolet radiation-busting abilities.

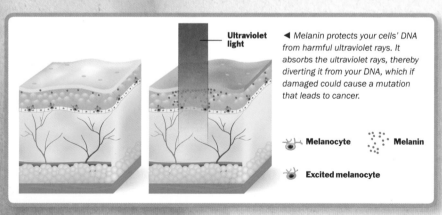

Ultraviolet light

◄ *Melanin protects your cells' DNA from harmful ultraviolet rays. It absorbs the ultraviolet rays, thereby diverting it from your DNA, which if damaged could cause a mutation that leads to cancer.*

Melanocyte　　**Melanin**

Excited melanocyte

SKIN COLOUR

All people, irrespective of skin colour, have the same number of melanocytes. What determines the darkness of your skin is how active the melanocytes are and the number of dendrites available to reach other cells. Dark-skinned people have larger melanocytes that produce more melanin, and with more dendrites they have a much greater reach.

Contrary to what you might think, if you have albinism, you do have melanocytes. However, a genetic mutation affects the ability of your melanocytes to produce or distribute melanin, which causes your keratinocytes to be devoid of pigment.

Moles, or naevi, arise when groups of melanocytes cluster together. Freckles are formed when groups of keratinocytes are fed lots of melanosomes produced by an ultraviolet-overexposed and hyperactive melanocyte.

▶ *Freckles are more prevalent in people with pale skin, and particularly with red hair, due to their possessing variants of gene MC1R.*

DERMIS

The epidermis is avascular, which means that it does not have any blood vessels. This is why superficial scrapes to your skin do not bleed or hurt terribly. If, however, a scrape removes the epidermis, it will reveal a flash of a brilliant white layer, then bleeding will begin. The scrape, which may result in a permanent scar, has reached the dermis, which is where all the skin's maintenance apparatus is found, as well as an infrastructure of blood and lymphatic vessels.

This thick layer of connective tissue is solely responsible for nourishing the epidermis. It uses the twinned protein fibres collagen and elastin to provide a strong and elastic scaffold that allows your skin to stretch and contract. In between these fibres, a mixed bag of residents occupies the spaces.

PAPILLAE

Papillae are tiny dermal projections, or bumps, that stick up from the dermis into the epidermis. They are particularly prominent in the skin surface of the hands and feet, where they give rise to the whirls and loops that make your fingerprints. Microscopically, they exist

as coils of tiny blood vessels (capillaries) arranged vertically in arches – these create the pinpricks of blood that appear when you graze your skin. Dermal papillae feed the epidermis and contain touch-sensitive receptors called Meissner's corpuscles that help you discriminate light touch.

SENSORY RECEPTORS

Nerves within the dermis also penetrate the epidermis, allowing both layers to transmit sensations to your brain. Most of the sensory receptors respond to pressure, temperature and touch. These specially adapted nerve endings are buried at varying depths within the dermis so you can respond to different kinds of touch. The slightest disturbance or distortion triggers a nerve impulse that will either stop firing so that you forget about it (for example, clothes against your skin) or continue firing to get your attention, as when you are in pain.

▼ *Your ability to discriminate touch, superficial pain and heat are down to these structures within your dermis.*

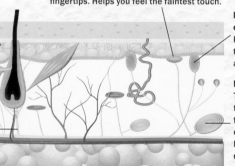

Free nerve ending:
Have no special covering and extend into the epidermis. Helps you feel pain, temperature and pressure changes.

Merkel's disk: Found at the base of the epidermis, especially in the lips and fingertips. Helps you feel the faintest touch.

Meissner's corpuscle: Helps you feel texture, pressure and vibrations.

Hair follicle receptor:
Nerve fibre endings that wrap around the base of the hair. Act as mechanoreceptors, allowing you to feel changes in air current or objects that brush against your hair.

Pacinian corpuscle:
The largest of the receptors, found deep in the dermis and joints. Helps you sense deep sustained pressures, tickles and fast vibrations.

SWEAT GLANDS

It is often said, in jest, that horses sweat, men perspire, and women glow. A remnant of Victorian polite society perhaps, or a scientific truth? One Japanese study conducted in 2010 concluded that it might just be so, after finding that the women in their small cohort of 37 test subjects needed to raise their body temperature before they could sweat, whereas the men had a more immediate sweating response, believed to be enhanced by testosterone.

▲ You have millions of sweat pores (shown here in a micrograph), which form coiled tubes at the base of the dermis.

These conclusions were challenged by other scientists in the field, who identified limitations in the study and maintained that absolute power and not gender governed the sweat response. Generalizations and arguments aside, the fact is that we all sweat or perspire even at rest, but do not always notice. It is all down to a long, coiled, hollow tube of epidermal cells called the sweat gland.

Around 3,000,000 sweat glands can be found on your skin, releasing their watery secretions to help you literally cool down and keep your body temperature constant, or to metaphorically cool down your nerves. Either way, your sweat glands are at the command of your nervous system.

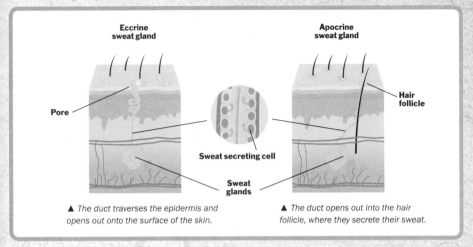

Eccrine sweat gland

Apocrine sweat gland

Pore

Hair follicle

Sweat secreting cell

Sweat glands

▲ The duct traverses the epidermis and opens out onto the surface of the skin.

▲ The duct opens out into the hair follicle, where they secrete their sweat.

The coiled segment of the sweat gland sits deep in the dermis, while the duct helps transports the sweat to the skin surface. Not all sweat glands are alike, as your nose may tell you. There are two distinct types:

Apocrine: These sweat glands are found in the hair-bearing regions of your skin, such as your armpits and groin, including the area around the nipples. These glands are stimulated during puberty to produce sweat of a distinctive odour, caused by bacteria on your skin breaking down the protein, fat and sugar components of sweat, and the musky aroma of pheromones that are associated with sexual attraction.

Eccrine: Eccrine sweat glands are more abundant and are found across the rest of your body (especially your palms and soles), except on your lips and certain parts of your genitals. They secrete mostly water, salt and other waste products, including small amounts of urea. On a hot day, you could lose around 2l (4 pints) of sweat. The reason you cool down is that sweat uses your body's heat to energize its evaporation. Earwax, or cerumen, is another type of secretion produced by an altered sweat gland in the ear called the ceruminous gland. This produces a sticky wax-like secretion made up of sweat and the oily substance sebum, which acts as a barrier to protect your ear drum.

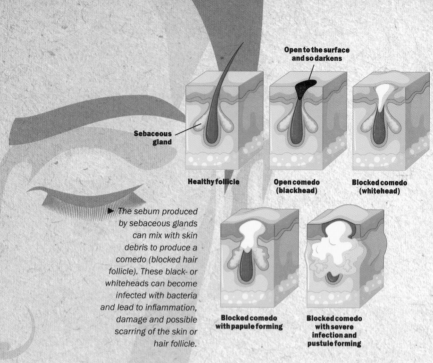

Open to the surface and so darkens

Sebaceous gland

Healthy follicle

Open comedo (blackhead)

Blocked comedo (whitehead)

Blocked comedo with papule forming

Blocked comedo with severe infection and pustule forming

▶ *The sebum produced by sebaceous glands can mix with skin debris to produce a comedo (blocked hair follicle). These black- or whiteheads can become infected with bacteria and lead to inflammation, damage and possible scarring of the skin or hair follicle.*

SEBACEOUS GLANDS

Sebaceous glands give you zits. Mind you, this is only when they are blocked or infected. These specialized epidermal cells are the source of your body's natural moisturizers. They are found all over, except in your eyelids, and attach to the hair follicle, where they secrete the oily, fatty substance sebum to help lubricate your skin and hair. If you leave your hair or face unwashed for several days, that grease buildup is sebum.

As well as also keeping the skin waterproof, sebum creates a hostile environment for certain bacteria and fungi because, by mixing with sweat, it makes the skin surface more acidic. How much sebum you ooze is determined by your sex hormones. These become active after puberty, which is why the teenage years are characteristically spotty.

HAIR MUSCLES

You will find all four types of tissue in your skin: epithelial, nervous, connective and muscular (see pages 44–45). The muscles are in the form of the arrector pili. These small bundles of smooth muscle, which you cannot control, are arranged in a 'diagonal' orientation next to the hair follicles. When you are cold or scared, these muscles contract, tugging the base of your hair and making it stand on end. This is called piloerection.

You probably know piloerection by the name 'goosebumps', which served a very useful function when our ancestors looked like yetis. These days, piloerection is more useful to hairy animals because, by trapping air close to the body, it increases insulation. It also makes them appear more imposing when confronted with a flight or fight scenario. Luckily, we do not have goosebumps on our face, including our eyebrows, eyelashes, moustache and nose, because these hairs lack any muscle.

▼ Goosebumps are an evolutionary remnant of our hairy ape days of the past.

HYPODERMIS

The term 'hypodermis' comes from the Greek words meaning 'beneath the skin'. The hypodermis is often referred to as the subcutaneous fat layer or superficial fascia. Although it is not technically part of your skin, the hypodermis connects your skin with the rest of your body, and merges with the connective tissues that cover your muscles.

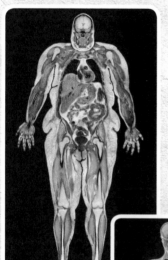

▲ Visceral fat, linked with a serious condition called metabolic syndrome, arises when an excess of white fat wraps around organs.

▶ An MRI shows the distribution of white fat in a slim woman.

Mostly consisting of fat (adipose tissue), blood vessels and protein fibres, the hypodermis serves several different functions:

- The collagen fibres of the hypodermis allow your skin to move across the underlying muscle tissue with ease.

- Its heavy fat content acts as insulation, a shock absorber and an energy reserve.

- Adipose tissue is a major hormone-secreting endocrine organ. It produces a small amount of oestrogen in both men and women, as well as the hormone leptin, which helps control your hunger. It also has receptors that enable it to respond to signals from other endocrine organs and the nervous system.

FAT TYPES

In a healthy adult, around 50 per cent of the hypodermis is made up of fat. This type of fat is known as white fat, and is what accumulates around your body when you put on weight. In contrast, brown fat, also called brown adipose tissue, is located in the front and back of the neck and your upper back. These fat cells contain lots of mitochondria, which themselves contain iron and give it a brown hue. Your body uses brown fat to burn calories to generate heat and does not store it as additional calories, as it does in white fat. Exercising, sleep and exposure to cold temperatures can help increase levels of brown fat as opposed to white fat.

AGEING SKIN

One of the benefits or drawbacks of your skin is that it provides a visible account of the ageing process. Age-related changes to your skin typically occur by the time you reach thirty years old. The process can accelerate depending on your lifestyle and excesses.

As you age, your skin gradually loses its elasticity as the cells shrink in size, and increasing abnormalities crop up in both the epidermis and dermis. Thinning of the epidermis occurs in part when the basal layer slows down its production of new cells until it can no longer keep up with the rate at which cells are lost from the cornified layer. In the dermis, the collagen and elastin fibres, which normally provide a strong scaffold for the skin, begin to weaken and eventually buckle, causing wrinkles to appear on your skin. Changes in the hypodermis include the loss of fat, especially in the hands and feet, which accentuates the dermal changes and leads to sagging. The loss of cushioning also makes your blood vessels more vulnerable to rupture and bruising.

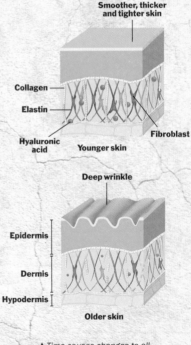

▲ Time causes changes to all three layers of skin.

AREN'T YOU HAIRY?

Your hair is just a modified version of dead epidermal cells, and yet for many people it provides a source of extreme confidence and despair in equal measure. About 5,000,000 of these protein filaments erupt through your skin surface. Most people with a full head of hair have over 100,000 strands on their head.

▲ This eyelash has been magnified many times.

Hair serves many functions, including:
- Providing insulation
- Preventing harmful microbes entering via the nose or ears
- Protecting underlying structures from the sun, which explains why your scalp has the highest density to protect your most treasured organ, the brain

HAIR STRUCTURE

Shaft: Your hair develops in a similar fashion to the top layer of your skin. The visible part of your hair strand, or shaft, is a specialized form of keratin. It consists of three different layers: a spongy inner core (medulla), a middle cortex and an outer, transparent cuticle layer. All the cells in the shaft are dead.

Follicle: The shaft is anchored in the skin with the help of a tube of epidermal cells called the hair follicle that invaginates (or is folded back in on itself) into the dermis. The shape of your hair follicles determines whether your hair is curly, straight or wavy, as they mould the hidden part of the strand, the hair root.

Bulb: As you descend further into the hair root, it takes on a bulb-like shape, a bit like a spring onion. The bulb is the site of hair manufacture, where a germinal layer of basal keratinocytes continually churn out new cells that push those above further up and away from the life-giving nourishment provided by the hair papilla. The papilla is a structure at the base of the hair follicle where tiny blood vessels provide blood, oxygen and nutrients to the hair bulb. The basal cells in the hair bulb are among your most rapidly dividing cells. During your development, their active profile forces the epidermal cells to extend deeper into the dermis to secure a good blood supply.

Melanocytes are also present here, feeding melanin into the root cells and subsequently colouring the inner and middle regions of the hair shaft.

Plexus: Clasping the hair bulb is the plexus, which is a fancy name for a network of sensory nerves that help you feel hair movements.

▼ *From straight hair to afro hair, your hair type is governed by the shape of your hair follicles.*

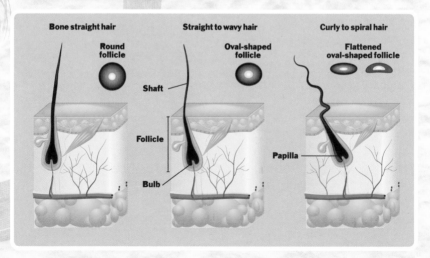

Bone straight hair — Round follicle — Shaft — Follicle — Bulb

Straight to wavy hair — Oval-shaped follicle

Curly to spiral hair — Flattened oval-shaped follicle — Papilla

HAIR GROWTH

The cells that make your hair are among your body's most active, so they sometimes need a break. This is why your hair enters periodic cycles of active growth and rest before it falls out. Each hair follicle can go through this cycle at least 25 times in its lifespan.

Anagen: The length of the active growth phase, also known as anagen, varies depending on the hair's location. It lasts between 2 and 6 years for hairs on your scalp, but weeks or months in other areas, such as your eyebrows or legs, which explains their short length. During anagen, hair follicles are stimulated by various growth factors to produce new cells. Over 80 per cent of your scalp hair is in this phase at any one time. Hair on your scalp grows about 1.25cm (½in) every month. The higher levels of the female hormone oestrogen during pregnancy is known to prolong this phase and give women thicker and longer hair.

Catagen: The hair follicle then enters the next phase, catagen, which marks the end of active growth. The follicle shrinks, or involutes, causing the hair bulb to pull away from the root and its nourishment. This short phase lasts only 2 to 3 weeks.

Telogen: No growth occurs for several weeks, then the hair follicle is reactivated to produce new hair and pushes the old hair out, causing it to shed when combed or washed. Around 50 to 100 hairs on your head are lost this way every day.

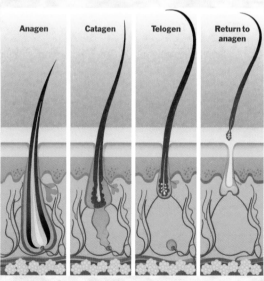

► This illustration shows the three phases of hair growth. The maximal length your hair can grow is determined by the amount of time it stays in the anagen phase.

HAIR LOSS

Anything that interferes with or damages the hair follicle can result in reduced hair growth and loss (alopecia):

- Ageing affects the number of hair follicles that can be reactivated.
- Stress can induce more hair follicles to enter the telogen phase, resulting in increased shedding.
- The hormone dihydrotestosterone (DHT), derived from the primary male sex hormone testosterone, is thought to shrink the hair follicles in men (and some women) who are genetically sensitive to its effects. This results in reduced hair growth and classic male pattern baldness.
- The common skin condition called folliculitis causes bacteria or fungus to infect the hair follicle, causing it to inflame and fill with pus, forming red and painful pustules.
- Areata alopecia causes your own immune cells to target your hair follicles, making them shrink.

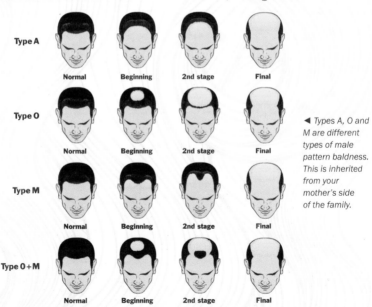

Type A

Normal   Beginning   2nd stage   Final

Type O

Normal   Beginning   2nd stage   Final

Type M

Normal   Beginning   2nd stage   Final

Type O+M

Normal   Beginning   2nd stage   Final

◀ *Types A, O and M are different types of male pattern baldness. This is inherited from your mother's side of the family.*

HAIR SHADE

Three things determine hair colour – hair stylists not included. Melanocytes, the sun and your age engender your hair with chameleon-like qualities.

Melanocytes: With the help of an enzyme called tyrosinase, melanocytes in your hair follicles produce two types of melanin pigment: a pale version called pheomelanin and a dark version called eumelanin. If you have blond hair, your melanocytes produce pheomelanin. If you have brunette or black hair, your melanocytes produce lots of eumelanin. If you have hair that lies in between these colours, you produce a mixture of both versions of melanin.

▼ *Black and brunette are the most common hair colours in the world.*

Sunshine: When it comes to your skin, the sun and your melanocytes have a special kind of relationship, but this does not extend to your hair. Normally, when the sun hits your skin, it causes the melanin to become oxidized, which melanocytes will absolutely not stand for, so they respond by producing more melanin, which is why your skin gets darker. However, when the sun hits the melanin in your hair shaft and oxidizes it, over time it gets lighter (or bleached) because there are no melanocytes in the shaft to counteract the effect.

Ageing: Grey hair arises because, as you age, the enzyme tyrosinase slows down its activity and produces very little pigment. You go completely white when tyrosinase fully retires and no longer produces any pigment at all.

▲ Your hair colour is governed by the type and amount of melanin your melanocytes produce.

◄ Grey hair can also arise when white hair is dispersed among your normal pigmented hairs. White hair is generally a sign that the enzyme tyrosinase has aged and stopped working.

NAILS

They are not just for scratching or picking your nose. These transparent horny splints of keratin protect your outermost extremities – your fingers and toes – and help you grab and pick at things.

STRUCTURE

The structure and growth of your nails is similar to that of your hair:

Nail body: The part you paint with varnish is the nail body. Like your hair shaft, your nail body is formed of dead cells. However, the cells in your nails contain more keratin and are tightly packed, which makes your nails extremely hard.

Nail root: It all starts in the nail root, or matrix, which you cannot see because it is embedded in a groove in your skin. The epidermal cells here are constantly dividing, causing nails to grow up to 5mm (⅕ in) every month. New cells push the older ones along. These thicken with keratin, die and form the nail body, which rests on the skin of the nail bed.

Lunula: This is the part of the nail root that you can see, most clearly on your thumb. It is a crescent-shaped area that appears white due to its thickness, obscuring the tiny blood vessels of the nail bed beneath.

Cuticle: The nail root and matrix are sealed by the cuticle, an almost transparent layer of skin. This thin band of dead epithelial cells adheres to the nail body.

Free edge: The free edge of the nail, or tip, is the opaque area that typically grows long. Your fingernails grow much faster than your toenails, in part because the longer the bone at the end of the digit, the faster the rate of growth.

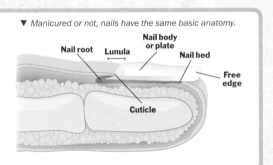

▼ Manicured or not, nails have the same basic anatomy.

Nail root
Lunula
Nail body or plate
Nail bed
Free edge
Cuticle

REVEALING YOUR HEALTH

Nails have another great benefit: they can indicate your general state of health. That is because your body diverts specific nutrients away from your nails when the rest of your body needs them. If your diet has lacked protein, this will show months later as pale patches in your nail, often referred to as milk spots but medically known as leukonychia. Tiny red splinter-like streaks under the nail, called splinter haemorrhages, could indicate a possible infection of your heart called infective endocarditis, although less sinister causes could explain their presence. Infective endocarditis is associated with clots from your heart migrating to other areas, including the tiny blood vessels of the nail bed.

▼ When your doctor looks at your nails, they are looking for potential signs of ill health. Disease and deficiencies can alter the way your nails look and grow.

CHAPTER 4

MOVE YOUR BODY

THE MUSCULOSKELETAL SYSTEM

Long ago, muscular and skeletal systems were wedded to support each other in the pursuit of locomotion. Your bones do many things, but they need your muscles to move, as without them conscious movement will not occur.

MUSCLES

Muscles come in three different forms and belong to two different groups. Skeletal muscle is the type most commonly associated with the term muscle, and as its name implies it is wedded to the skeleton. It is also referred to as voluntary muscle because you control whether it moves. The movement of smooth and cardiac muscles are not under your direct control, so they are also known as involuntary muscle. Smooth and cardiac muscles are explained in Chapter 5, page 113.

CONNECTIVE TISSUE

The musculoskeletal system relies heavily on connective tissue to work, and shamelessly pimps it out in different forms for its own gain. Your bones are connected to other bones through an elastic fibrous connective tissue called ligaments, and the spaces that form in between these bones are called joints, which are covered in a rubbery connective tissue called cartilage. Your muscles are connected to your bones through a tough fibrous connective tissue called tendons. Muscles are also connected to each other by a specialized type of connective tissue called fascia, which binds and holds them together.

THE SKELETON

Your gang of bones is 206 members strong – the largest is your thigh bone, or femur, and the smallest is the stapes in the middle ear. More than half the bones in your entire body are found in your hands and feet. In fact, you had many more bones when you were a baby, but several fused together after their main jobs were done.

Without bones you would be a shapeless, slug-like mound of fat, skin and muscular matter with no ability to protect your vital organs from any potential impact. In addition to their locomotive functions and shielding your heart, lungs and central nervous system (brain and spinal cord), your bones also help you breathe, stop you from bleeding to death and fight infection. How? By providing the floorspace for producing your blood cells, deep in the bone marrow.

It does not stop there. Your bones are reservoirs for key minerals such as calcium and phosphates that get released into the blood when your body most needs them.

How much are you loving your skeleton right now?

THE SKELETON

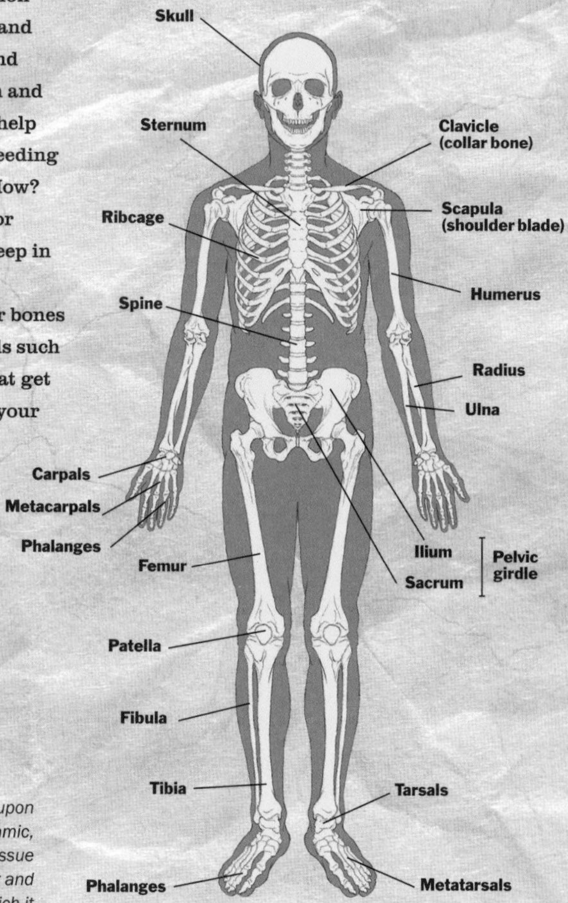

- Skull
- Sternum
- Ribcage
- Spine
- Clavicle (collar bone)
- Scapula (shoulder blade)
- Humerus
- Radius
- Ulna
- Carpals
- Metacarpals
- Phalanges
- Femur
- Ilium
- Sacrum
- Pelvic girdle
- Patella
- Fibula
- Tibia
- Tarsals
- Phalanges
- Metatarsals

▶ *Your bones are like a scaffold upon which your flesh hangs. This dynamic, living and rigid connective tissue continually remodels itself to repair and regenerate old worn-out bone, which it dissolves and replaces with new tissue.*

THE AXIAL SKELETON

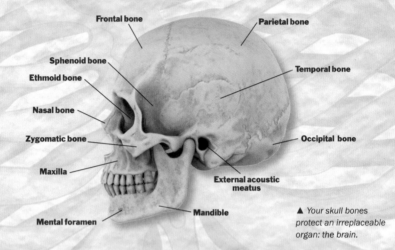

Frontal bone

Parietal bone

Sphenoid bone

Temporal bone

Ethmoid bone

Nasal bone

Zygomatic bone

Occipital bone

Maxilla

External acoustic meatus

Mental foramen

Mandible

▲ *Your skull bones protect an irreplaceable organ: the brain.*

Your bones are customarily divided into two types of skeleton. Your axial skeleton encompasses your skull, spine, ribs and breastbone. Draw a line downward from the top of your head and these bones are the ones that form the vertical central axis of your body, protecting your central nervous system and inner organs. Your appendicular skeleton comprises all those bones that 'append' to the central axis.

SKULL

Your skull protects your brain and sensory organs. Your eyes are dunked into deep sockets and the smell-detecting part of your olfactory system is in the nasal cavity. There are different ways of describing the bones of the skull. If defined according to moveable regions, you have the cranium and the mandible

(lower jaw). Alternatively, you can classify according to what the bones protect: the neurocranium describes the round bit of the head, including the forehead, that houses the brain and brainstem; the viscerocranium describes your facial bones that protect your sensory organs and provide a framework for your face muscles to attach.

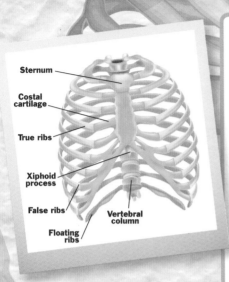

▲ The seven pairs of true ribs connect to your sternum directly via costal cartilages. The three pairs of false ribs connect to your sternum via the seventh rib. The final two pairs of floating ribs can be missing in some people.

RIBCAGE

Your ribcage comprises 12 pairs of curved bones that protect the heart and lungs. Ribs are named true, false and floating, depending on the extent of attachment to the breastbone or spine. The breastbone, or sternum, has a little piece of bone that sticks out, called the xiphoid process, which medical professionals use as a landmark to orientate themselves to perform chest compressions during resuscitation attempts.

SPINE

Your spine, or vertebral column, has 33 vertebrae. It supports your torso and head and provides a base for rib attachment. The vertebral column is curved to distribute your weight evenly. The upper 24 vertebrae are articulating, helping you bend and twist. There are three types of articulating vertebrae that exhibit differences in structure to manage the levels of pressure exerted: cervical, thoracic and lumbar. The lower spine comprises two types of fused vertebrae: sacrum and coccyx.

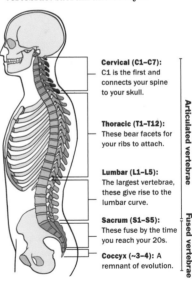

Cervical (C1–C7): C1 is the first and connects your spine to your skull.

Thoracic (T1–T12): These bear facets for your ribs to attach.

Lumbar (L1–L5): The largest vertebrae, these give rise to the lumbar curve.

Sacrum (S1–S5): These fuse by the time you reach your 20s.

Coccyx (~3–4): A remnant of evolution.

Articulated vertebrae

Fused vertebrae

WHAT'S IN A BONE?

Getting your teeth around bones is not as easy as dogs make out. Let's look at the femur. The shaft of a long bone is called the diaphysis, while the bulbous ends are epiphyses.

MARROW

Dogs are no fools because bones are full of good stuff, or bone marrow, of which there are two kinds. Inside the cavity of the diaphysis is the yellow marrow, containing an abundance of fat cells. In adults, yellow marrow fat contains stem cells that produce bone and cartilage. It sits on the reserve bench of blood production too. Red bone marrow produces all the different cells of your blood.

CORTICAL AND CANCELLOUS BONE

Two types of bone, or osseous tissue, make your skeleton. Walls of the diaphysis are made of cortical bone that is compact and tough to support heavy weights without breaking. As you move to the epiphyses, an inner layer of spongy cancellous bone predominates, filled with red bone marrow.

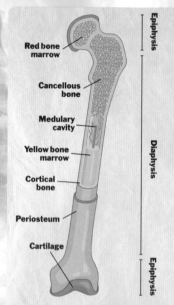

▲ Inside a typical long bone are structures and tissues that store minerals and produce your blood.

PERIOSTEUM

Lining the surface of your skeleton is the periosteum, a double-layered membrane of connective tissue. The outer layer is fibrous and contains collagen; it is where muscles, tendons and ligaments attach. It contains nerves as well as blood and lymphatic vessels that give nutrients to compact bone. The underlying cellular layer contains the stem cells, called osteogenic cells, that give rise to osteoblasts, the bone-making cells.

BONE CELLS

Osteogenic cells: These stems cells are the only bone cells that can divide. They form the inner coat of the endosteum.

Osteoblasts: Bone is the matrix produced by osteoblasts. This secretion is a framework of collagen protein fibres, to which calcium phosphate salts stick and harden.

Osteocytes: Bone is monitored and managed by more mature versions of osteoblasts called osteocytes, which ripen when osteoblasts trap themselves within the matrix. Osteocytes sit in small spaces within the matrix called lacunae. Osteocytes are oval, centipede-like cells that extend their cytoplasm through small canals, or canaliculi, which allows them to link and communicate with each other and exchange nutrients and waste.

Osteoclasts: The osteoclast is not of osteogenic origin but rather a second-generation white blood cell and descendant of macrophages (see pages 148–51). These cells are also present in the periosteum and endosteum, and work in harmony with osteoblasts to ensure that the breakdown and reabsorption of existing bone does not exceed the formation of new tissue, which would result in osteoporosis.

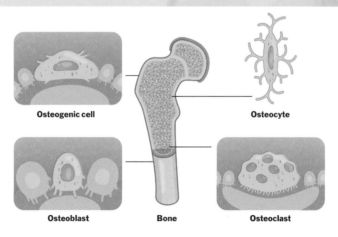

Osteogenic cell

Osteocyte

Osteoblast

Bone

Osteoclast

▲ *The four types of bone cells have specific roles.*

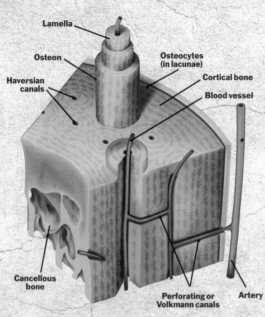

Lamella

Osteon

Haversian canals

Osteocytes (in lacunae)

Cortical bone

Blood vessel

Cancellous bone

Perforating or Volkmann canals

Artery

Different bones contain varying amounts of osseous tissue. Although cortical and cancellous bone are made of the same stuff, they vary in how their basic structural units are arranged.

◀ *Cortical bone forms a rigid, strong protective shell around cancellous bone. It comprises densely packed bone material.*

CORTICAL VS CANCELLOUS BONE

CORTICAL (COMPACT) BONE

This type of bone makes the outer wall of all your bones. It is the second hardest material in your body (after tooth enamel) and is responsible for 80 per cent of the weight of your bones. It is much denser than cancellous bone, and gives the exterior of bones their white, smooth appearance.

Cortical bone is made up of microscopic columns, called osteons, consisting of concentric rings of

osteocytes. Each of these rings is called a lamella. At the centre of each osteon is a Haversian canal, lined with endosteum containing nerves, blood and lymphatic vessels that also branch off to the inner and outer layers of the bone. Cortical bone is covered with periosteum.

CANCELLOUS (SPONGY) BONE

Cancellous bone is the internal tissue of bone, found in the ends of long bones, the pelvic bones, ribs, vertebrae in the

VERTEBRATES

▶ The crown for the vertebrate with the most bones probably goes to the snake.

Having an internal skeleton, or endoskeleton, is the defining characteristic of all vertebrates, both living and extinct. Vertebrates comprise humans and other mammals, amphibians, reptiles, birds and fish. Mammals have hundreds of bones. The blue whale has around 350 bones, while adult humans come in near the lower limit at 206 bones. Large snakes are thought to have up to 500 vertebrae, each attached to a pair of ribs, although most contain between 120 and 240 vertebrae on average.

spinal column and the skull. It is a porous network of open spaces, making it weaker and more flexible than compact bone. Cancellous bone has nearly ten times the surface area of cortical bone.

Cancellous bone is made up of rod or plate-like trabeculae, forming a mesh-like matrix. The surface of each trabecula is lined with endosteum. The growth pattern of trabeculae is in accordance to the stresses put on the bone. Spaces inside the trabeculae are filled with red bone marrow. There are no osteons, but the osteocytes occupy lacunae as they do in compact bone.

▲ When you run or jump, your bones do not normally break because the trabeculae of the cancellous bone absorbs the mechanical stress placed on your bones.

BONE SHAPES

As you have seen, your bones are distinguished according to where they live in your body and what they do. But how they look is also important because it determines how they work. There are five distinct bone shapes.

BONE TYPE	SHAPE	FUNCTION	EXAMPLES	
Long bones	Cylindrical, longer than they are wide	Confer mobility, strength and support, and house bone marrow	Upper and lower limbs, hands and feet	**Humerus**
Short bones	Cuboidal	Confer flexibility, by gliding over each other	Wrists (carpals) and tarsal bones	**Heel**
Flat bones	Thin and plate-like, often curved, with a large surface area	Protect underlying structures and organs, and act as muscle attachment sites	Cranial bones, shoulder blades, ribs and breastbone	**Scapula**
Sesamoid bones	Small, flat and round, most of them the size of a sesame seed	Developing inside tendons, these bones make the tendons stronger and prevent wear and tear as the joint moves	Patellas (knee), elbows, balls of feet and hands	**Patella**
Irregular bones	Complex, with large surface areas	Confer flexibility, and act as muscle and ligament attachment	Vertebrae of backbone and facial bones	**Vertebra**

MALE AND FEMALE SKELETONS

The overall skeleton is more delicate in women compared to men. However, determining the sex of bone material based on differences in shape alone is stifled by the natural variation that exists in humans. There are some interesting gender differences though:

BONE	GENDER DIFFERENCES
Pelvis	Wider in women and more boat-shaped, resulting in broader hips
Shoulders	Wider in men
Ribcage	Longer in men
Cranium	More robust in men to accommodate the heavier muscle attachment; brow bone also more prominent. Women keep many of the bone traits they had prior to puberty, causing their facial features to remain smoother.
Chin and jaw	More prominent and angular in men

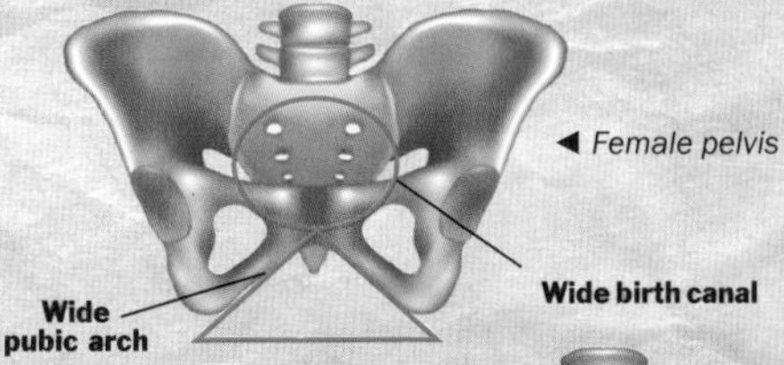

◀ *Female pelvis*

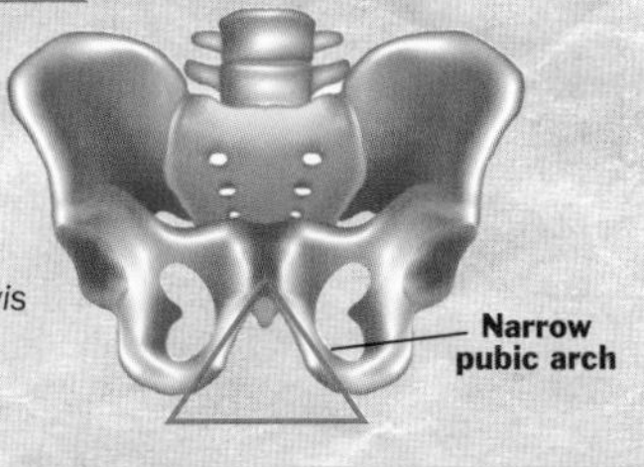

Wide pubic arch

Wide birth canal

▶ *Male pelvis*

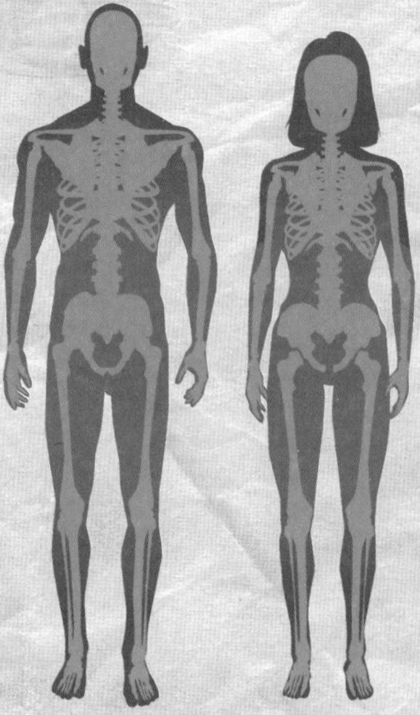

Narrow pubic arch

▲ *Male and female skeletons show differences in form and size.*

CARTILAGE

Your bone delegates its roles to cartilage wherever it needs to be more flexible. This smooth, tough and agile connective tissue pops up in all your adult joints, where it covers the ends of your bones, replacing the periosteum.

Similarly to bone, cartilage is produced by cells that make a matrix, called chondroblasts, and is maintained by their more mature versions, chondrocytes, which are embedded within it and sit in lacunae. Microscopically, chondrocytes look like googly eyes fixed in a bed made of a protein-carbohydrate ground substance containing collagen and/or elastin. Being avascular, or not served by blood vessels, they get their nutrients by way of diffusion through a dense connective tissue called the perichondrium. This membrane covers the cartilage and is one of the reasons why it is so slow to heal when damaged.

▼ *This micrograph shows the structure of your outer ear with elastic cartilage sandwiched between the perichondrium.*

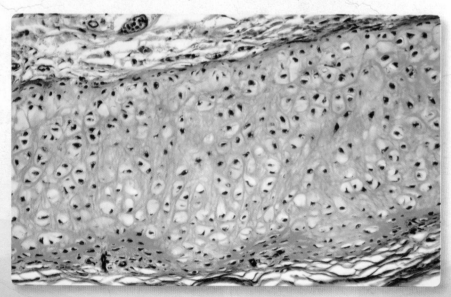

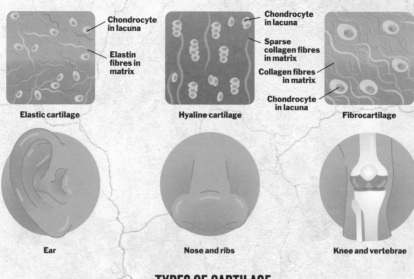

Elastic cartilage
- Chondrocyte in lacuna
- Elastin fibres in matrix

Hyaline cartilage
- Chondrocyte in lacuna
- Sparse collagen fibres in matrix

Fibrocartilage
- Collagen fibres in matrix
- Chondrocyte in lacuna

Ear

Nose and ribs

Knee and vertebrae

TYPES OF CARTILAGE

There are three types of cartilage:

Hyaline cartilage: Hyaline cartilage formed your immature skeleton, and remained as a special plate, responsible for growth, within the epiphysis of your long bones. Hyaline cartilage also forms a thin lining on the articulating surfaces of your bones. In addition, it is present at the end of your nose and in parts of the respiratory tract: the voice box, windpipe and rings of your bronchi (see page 171). Hyaline cartilage's collagen fibres are sparsely arranged, rendering it smooth and slippery.

Fibrocartilage: This type of cartilage cushions the bones of the spine and is present at the knee joint. Fibrocartilage contains many bundles of collagen, which makes it particularly tough and strong.

Elastic cartilage: Forming your outer ears and your epiglottis, which closes your windpipe when you swallow, elastic cartilage has an additional protein that predominates – elastin. This protein adds flexibility and explains why your ears can bend then snap back.

BONE DEVELOPMENT

As a fetus, your bones started out as solid cartilage. Later, as you grew, they hollowed out and hardened. This follows a basic law of structural engineering: hollowing out a tubular structure causes a slight reduction in strength but a dramatic reduction in weight – a hugely desirable model that the rest of your musculoskeletal system appreciates. The process of replacing cartilage with bone, called ossification, occurs first in the shaft of the long bones, followed by the ends of the bones, where it results in the formation of spongy bone.

EPIPHYSEAL PLATE

During your infancy, soft discs of hyaline cartilage in the region where the epiphysis meets the diaphysis (called the metaphysis) undergo rapid cell division. Known as the growth plate or epiphyseal plate, this is the site where your bones begin to lengthen. New cells push older cells toward the centre, causing them to get squashed and harden. As this continues, the bone gradually elongates and you get taller.

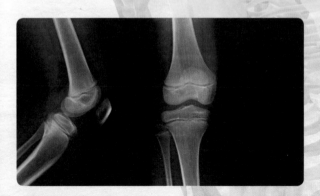

◄ The epiphyseal plate shows up as an invisible line in an X-ray. In an adult, it has hardened and shows up as a white line. Bones still grow in adulthood but only in diameter.

THE NEUROCRANIUM

The neurocranium is quite special because it is made of eight cranial bones, or plates, that were initially separate, but began to fuse together after we were born. This overlapping or drifting of plates served two purposes: to enable your head to flex and squeeze through your mother's birth canal, and to accommodate the high rate at which your brain grows during childhood.

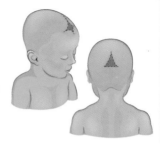

▲ Fontanelles are soft spaces between the cranial bones of babies and infants which have yet to fuse fully.

STOPS AND STARTS

By the age of four, your brain is acquiring information at a phenomenal pace. This requires a huge amount of energy, so your body reaches a point where it cannot sustain the growth of both brain and body. A decision is made to temporarily slow down your bone growth so that your brain can consume the energy resources it needs to grow.

Once you reach puberty, your body switches its priorities as the brain has grown to the point where it needs fewer resources. Almost as a gesture of thanks, the brain releases a surge of sex hormones from the hypothalamus and pituitary gland, which triggers the final growth spurt. Your epiphyseal plates once again churn out new cells at a rapid pace. This continues until your late teens or early twenties. Then, the growth plate stops dividing, calcifies and hardens. It fuses with its neighbouring bone cells to form the epiphyseal line. This is visible in X-rays as the point where the diaphysis meets the epiphysis.

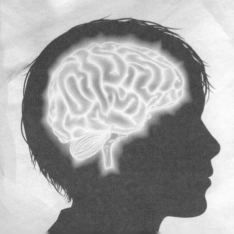

◀ Your final rapid growth spurt during puberty is initiated by the brain.

93

JOINTS AND LIGAMENTS

Joints are the sites where your bones meet other bones. Ligaments are stretchy bundles of connective tissue fibres that perform supportive roles in joints, the abdomen and breast tissue.

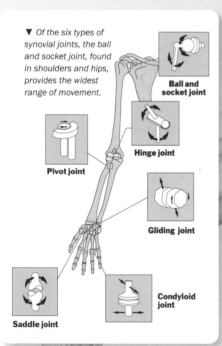

▼ Of the six types of synovial joints, the ball and socket joint, found in shoulders and hips, provides the widest range of movement.

Ball and socket joint

Hinge joint

Pivot joint

Gliding joint

Condyloid joint

Saddle joint

JOINT TYPES

Joints are a meeting place where bones can link up in a comfortable environment, with as little friction as possible. What happens at these bony venues depends on the type of joint.

Synovial joints: These are the most mobile joints and are found in your knee, elbow and hand bones. They are licenced to allow a large range of movement because they possess the synovium – a slippery coat of connective tissue that lines the joint. This one-cell-thick membrane produces synovial fluid that keeps the joint well oiled and prevents it from drying up. Synovial joints are encapsulated by tough gristle called the joint capsule, which helps the joint maintain its integrity and prevents any abnormal movements. Synovial joints fall into one of six groups depending on their type of movement: hinge, gliding (or plane), pivot, ball and socket, saddle and condyloid.

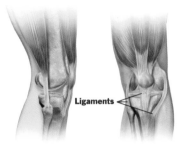

▲ *Ligaments join two pieces of bone.*

Fibrous joints: These joints are generally fixed and do not move. Examples include the joints in the fetal skull known as sutures, which use fibrous tissue to join the cranial bones together (see page 93). These remain flexible to accommodate the growing brain until the growth rate slows down and the sutures start the fusion process, becoming immovable.

Cartilaginous joints: These use cartilage to connect two bones together, which confers partial mobility over short distances. Your rib bones connect in this way to your sternum, which is the reason they can expand. As in most things, though, there is always one exception: the intervertebral discs of your spine. Although they are fibrous joints, they also contain cartilage (they are fibrocartilaginous, see page 91), which makes them semi-mobile.

LIGAMENT ROLES

Ligaments are bundles of collagen and elastin protein fibres, which are made by fibroblast cells. These cells sit between the fibres they produce and are fed by the spongy tissue carrying blood vessels and nerves that is positioned between the bundles. Musculoskeletal ligaments penetrate the periosteum to join the two bones together that make a joint. Ligaments also stop bones from dislocating by restricting their movement.

The organs in your abdomen do not just float around: they are held in place by various structures, including peritoneal ligaments. Ligaments also help maintain the shape and integrity of the female breast.

SKELETAL MUSCLES

Sticks and stones may break your bones, but luckily bones have muscles to support them. Without muscles, you would not be able to move. These soft tissues, joined to your skeleton through tough connective tissue tendons, create movement by contracting and relaxing. There are well over 600 distinct muscles in your body that vary in their size, shape and function.

The nomenclature used to describe muscles may seem quite random at first, so it might help to know that the rationale behind their names is based on features of the muscles themselves.

Skeletal muscles vary in their size. The largest are your glutes, which form your buttocks, and the smallest is the stapedius muscle inside your ear, which is about 1mm (¹⁄₂₅in) long. Size differences arise due to variations in the number of individual muscle cell fibres, the fibre's diameter, the length of the muscle's belly (central part) or how much work it does. Therefore, in some muscle groups you will find reference to the terms 'major' or 'minor'. For example, the pectoralis major is the larger of the two muscles of your chest.

In terms of a muscle's location, anatomical position labels apply, so the tibialis anterior refers to the front (anterior) muscle of your shin bone

(tibia). A muscle's shape can also be used to name it, so the deltoid muscle of your shoulder relates to its delta-like or triangular form. Your muscles can be named according to their movement, too. For example, the adductor longus of your thigh brings the thigh to the midline of your body, or adducts it. Finally, a muscle's number of heads, or points of origin, are also used for naming. Your biceps and triceps are so called because they have two and three heads respectively.

Most skeletal muscles mirror each other on the left and right sides of your body. They lie directly underneath your skin and attach to the hypodermis via a band or sheet of connective tissue called fascia. Although your skeletal muscles are associated with voluntary movements, they are involved in some involuntary movements, such as your reflexes (see page 101).

MAJOR MUSCLES

▼ *Here are some of the major skeletal muscles that help you move. Their names derive from aspects of their features, such as their size, location, shape and the movement they support.*

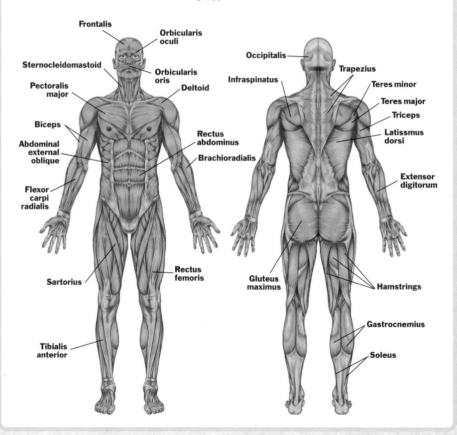

Frontalis
Orbicularis oculi
Sternocleidomastoid
Orbicularis oris
Pectoralis major
Deltoid
Biceps
Rectus abdominus
Abdominal external oblique
Brachioradialis
Flexor carpi radialis
Sartorius
Rectus femoris
Tibialis anterior

Occipitalis
Trapezius
Infraspinatus
Teres minor
Teres major
Triceps
Latissmus dorsi
Extensor digitorum
Gluteus maximus
Hamstrings
Gastrocnemius
Soleus

The cellular component of skeletal muscle is the myofibre, so called because of its long shape. Macroscopically, your muscles are arranged in bundles, wrapped in connective tissue called fascia. Fascia converges at the muscle ends to form tendons that attach muscles to your bones.

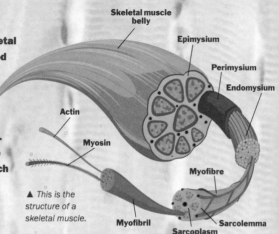

▲ This is the structure of a skeletal muscle.

MUSCLE ARCHITECTURE

MYOFIBRES

Long, slim myofibre cells have a nucleus that is spread across the edge of the cell membrane, or sarcolemma, to allow more space for the contractile units packed inside. Each myofibre contains smaller strands of fibres called myofibrils. These cylindrical bundles of protein, arranged parallel to each other, give skeletal muscle its striated microscopic appearance. Within each myofibril lie thousands of long-chained proteins called myofilaments that form the working unit of muscle. These proteins are the effector units of contraction because, like interlocking fingers, they overlap and slide across each other,

making the cell shorter – and thereby making the muscle contract. There are two types of myofilaments: actin and myosin, or actomyosin collectively.

FASCIA

Each muscle is made up of bundles of myofibres, which are covered by layers of dense connective tissue, or fascia. This connective tissue also wraps the whole muscle, allowing it to act independently, as well as myofibres within the muscle itself. The fascia carries nerves and blood vessels, which makes this tissue an indispensable part of your muscle machinery. There are three layers of fascia in skeletal muscle:

- Epimysium (covers the overall muscle)
- Perimysium (covers myofibre bundles)
- Endomysium (covers myofibres)

TENDONS

Tendons, also referred to as sinews, are tough inelastic cords of fascia at either end of the muscle. Tendons allow for optimum contractile movement. One end of a tendon attaches itself to the muscle belly while the other tethers to the target bone. Muscles often delegate some of their jobs to tendons, especially in areas where there are lots of joints and limited space, like the back of the hands. Here,

▲ There are no muscles in fingers, only tendons.

the muscles are situated higher up in the arm and act remotely, using the tendons as a remote control. Here are some key tendons:

Stapedial tendon (ear): Connects the smallest muscle (stapedius) to the smallest bone (stapes) in the middle ear.

Chordae tendineae (heart): Also known as the 'heart strings', these help keep heart valves in place.

Hamstring tendons (leg): Can be felt at the back of the knee.

Achilles tendon (feet): The strongest, thickest and largest tendon connects the large calf muscle (gastrocnemius) to the heel bone.

WHY SO RED?

The red colour of muscle is partly due to the iron-rich protein myoglobin. The iron in myoglobin binds to oxygen, which imparts a red colour, and allows your muscle fibres to hold their breath for longer. Muscle cells also contain lots of iron-rich mitochondria to meet its high energy demands, plus a dense network of blood capillaries.

▶ Myoglobin is closely related to haemoglobin.

NEUROMUSCULAR JUNCTIONS

Muscle movement usually feels automatic, and yet it involves a series of intricate events executed with precision. First, the brain generates an electrical nerve impulse, or action potential, that travels down from the motor cortex, through the spinal cord to motor nerves, which diverge into motor neurons, and stimulates individual myofibres in an area called the neuromuscular junction or motor end plate.

Motor neuron

An electrical signal reaches the synapse

Synaptic vesicle containing ACh

ACh binds to receptors on the sarcolemma

ACh depolarizes the sarcolemma

▲ At a neuromuscular junction, signals pass from a motor neuron to a myofibre.

A neuromuscular junction is a site where two different structures meet – one side is a motor neuron (a nerve cell forming a pathway along which impulses pass from the brain to a muscle) and the other is a muscle cell. Each myofibre is innervated by one motor neuron. The junction is, in fact, a synapse: a minute gap across which impulses pass by diffusion of a chemical substance, known as a neurotransmitter.

When an electrical signal reaches the synapse, it causes the release of the substance acetylcholine (ACh), which binds to protein receptors on the myofibre membrane, or sarcolemma. This causes the membrane to get all excited (depolarized) and for an electric current to pass through the membrane, resulting in the release of calcium within the cell that causes the microfilaments to slide over each other and interlock, and for the muscle to contract. A single motor neuron forms many synapses along the length of different myofibres, allowing the whole bundle to contract as a motor unit. To prevent your muscles being in a permanent state of contraction, the enzyme acetylcholinesterase breaks down ACh to relax them.

REFLEXES

Somatic reflexes, designed to protect you from potentially damaging interactions, are skeletal muscle movements that do not start in your brain. They are automatic involuntary movements that arise in response to an external trigger. Since reflexes bypass your brain, they are almost instantaneous. They are made possible by neural pathways called reflex arcs, that make use of two or three types of neurons: a sensory neuron, a motor neuron and sometimes an interneuron, which is a type of neuron that transmits impulses between other neurons.

Monosynaptic reflex arc: The simplest of reflex arcs, this involves a sensory and motor neuron. An example is the 'knee jerk reaction' set off by striking the patellar tendon, just below the knee. This stretches the tendon, which is picked up by stretch receptors in the muscle, which generate an impulse that is transmitted across a sensory neuron to a motor neuron in the spinal cord. The impulse travels from the motor neuron to the muscle – and the leg contracts. This reflex is concerned with keeping balance.

Polysynaptic reflex arc: This type of reflex arc involves a sensory neuron, interneuron and motor neuron. For example, the withdrawal reflex is set off when a stimulus causes pain in a finger. The pain is picked up by sensory receptors in the skin, which generate an impulse that is transmitted across a sensory neuron to a relay neuron in the spinal cord, which synapses with a motor neuron. When the motor nerves are activated, they send an impulse to the muscle – the arm contracts and flexes (bends).

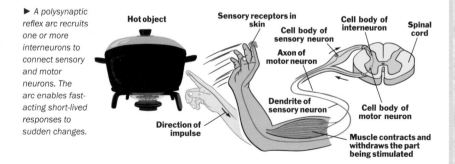

▶ A polysynaptic reflex arc recruits one or more interneurons to connect sensory and motor neurons. The arc enables fast-acting short-lived responses to sudden changes.

Hot object

Sensory receptors in skin

Cell body of sensory neuron

Axon of motor neuron

Cell body of interneuron

Spinal cord

Dendrite of sensory neuron

Cell body of motor neuron

Direction of impulse

Muscle contracts and withdraws the part being stimulated

MUSCLE CONTRACTION AND RELAXATION

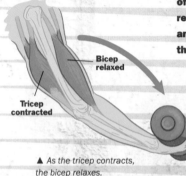

Bicep contracted

Tricep relaxed

Bicep relaxed

Tricep contracted

▲ *As the tricep contracts, the bicep relaxes.*

Your muscles have one job: to contract. When they work alone, they can only pull a bone, but when they work in pairs, they can draw the bone back to its original position. This requires oppositional pairs of agonist and antagonist muscles. To produce the reverse movement, the contracted muscle relaxes and the relaxed muscle contracts. The end result of their work is the flexing or extension of a joint.

A flexed joint is the medical term for bending: it results in the angle between the two bones of a joint decreasing. For example, when you flex your arms, your biceps contract and your triceps relax. An extended joint is equivalent to straightening: it causes the angle between the two bones of a joint to increase. Muscles that extend a joint are known as extensor muscles, while those that flex a joint are known as flexors.

TYPES OF MUSCLE CONTRACTION

If you try to lift more than your muscle can manage it contracts 'isometrically': the length of your muscle stays the same as the tension increases. In 'isotonic' contraction, where a manageable weight is lifted, the muscle length changes, either shortening or extending, while the tension remains the same. Your muscles have a resting level of tension, or tone, caused by the contraction of some motor units at rest, keeping the position of your bones and joints stable.

ENERGY FOR CONTRACTION

A myofibre can only shorten, or contract, to about half its resting length. It needs a significant amount of energy to move the actomyosin filaments. The myofibre gets this energy either aerobically in the presence of oxygen, or anaerobically in the absence of oxygen.

Aerobic respiration occurs in the mitochondria and uses oxygen to metabolize glucose and fatty acids to produce carbon dioxide and energy in the form of ATP (see page 30). A byproduct of this reaction is heat, which is why you get hot when you are exercising heavily.

Anaerobic respiration takes place in the fluid part of the cytoplasm (the cytosol) and produces lactic acid. This acid interferes with muscle contraction, leading to exhaustion and muscle burn. To get rid of the lactic acid, you breathe heavily to repay the oxygen debt, which converts the lactic acid back to glucose.

TYPES OF MUSCLE FIBRE

Myofibres are grouped into two types according to their ability to generate energy in the presence or absence of oxygen. Type 1 fibres are very slow to tire and are more abundant in long-distance runners. Type 2 fibres are more abundant in sprinters as they support short bursts of high-level activity. Type 2 fibres tire more quickly and rely on anaerobic respiration as they need to make energy more quickly than the body can supply oxygen.

	TYPE 1 OR SLOW TWITCH	TYPE 2 OR FAST TWITCH
Respiration	Aerobic	Anaerobic
Time to reach peak contraction	110 milliseconds	50 milliseconds
Myoglobin and mitochondria content	Higher	Lower

▶ Usain Bolt (far right) has many fast twitch fibres that produce small amounts of energy very quickly. Mo Farah (near right) relies on smaller slow twitch fibres that produce lots of energy very slowly.

MUSCLE TRAINING

Arnold Schwarzenegger famously said: 'I just use my muscles as a conversation piece, like someone walking a cheetah down 42nd Street.' If you've got, flaunt it. However, as we all know, we have not all got it to the same extent. The extent is down to training and genetics.

▲ The German showman Eugene Sandow is regarded as 'the Father of Modern Bodybuilding'. Born in 1867, he is believed to have organized the world's first bodybuilding competition.

Skeletal muscles are a bizarre tissue. One could go as far as saying they have slight masochistic tendencies because a bit of damage actually improves their performance. The 19th-century German philosopher Friedrich Nietzsche coined the phrase 'That which does not kill us, makes us stronger.' This is certainly the case when it comes to your muscles.

Muscle strength is defined as the amount of force that your muscle can produce in a single maximal effort. Training your muscles with different levels of resistance increases their strength by increasing the size and number of the individual myofibres. This arises because the repeat muscle contraction causes the myofibres to tear. Your body responds automatically to repair them using satellite stem cells in the extracellular matrix of the myofibres. Good rest causes the release of hormones that help the muscle heal and grow new fibres, which ultimately strengthens the muscle. In contrast, cardiovascular training increases your heart muscle strength not by new growth but by strengthening the existing cardiac fibres.

STRONGEST MUSCLE COMPETITION

These are the contenders:

Postural muscles: These include the muscles of your back (erector spinae), thigh (quadriceps femoris) and your buttocks (gluteus maximus), which all support joints or bones that are subject to gravity. These are large, strong muscles because of the amount of work they do, with the gluteus maximus the largest of all.

Cardiac muscle: Also known as the myocardium, this is the hardest-working muscle, as it constantly beats and never takes a break. This involuntary muscle constitutes the main tissue of the walls of the heart (see page 113).

Masseter muscles: With one on either side of the face, these muscles clench the jaw shut. The masseter connects the lower mandible (jawbone) and the cheekbone.

▶ *Among other things, the facial muscles allow us to express emotion.*

Winner? It is difficult to say because muscle strength can be measured in different ways and will also depend on each individual's diet, genetics and level of exercise.

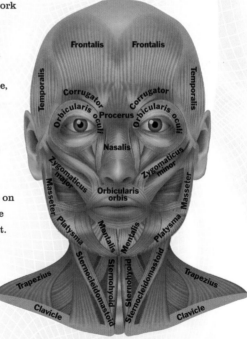

THE AGEING
MUSCULOSKELETAL SYSTEM

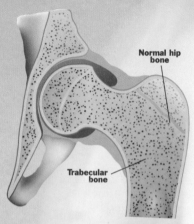

Normal hip bone

Trabecular bone

▲ In healthy bones, the trabecular plates and rods form strong networks.

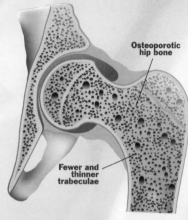

Osteoporotic hip bone

Fewer and thinner trabeculae

▲ In osteoporosis, there is loss of bone density and more disconnected rods.

Ageing is inevitable and is associated with the accumulation of genetic damage and exhaustion of stem cells. Ageing affects your musculoskeletal system in a number of specific ways. Debilitating diseases such as osteoporosis and osteoarthritis typify the ageing process.

CHANGES TO THE SKELETON

The loss of bone mass seen in osteoporosis is, in part, due to increases in the number of bone-eating osteoclasts and the amount of bone marrow fat, and the concomitant reduction of bone-producing osteoblasts and osteocytes. Consequently, your bone becomes unable to remodel and heal itself, causing it to sustain the altered shape and geometry induced by microcracks and microfractures. An associated decline in the levels of essential minerals, such as

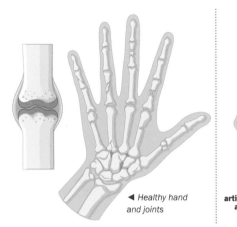

◄ Healthy hand and joints

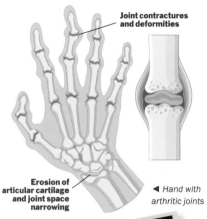

Joint contractures and deformities

Erosion of articular cartilage and joint space narrowing

◄ Hand with arthritic joints

calcium and phosphate stores, further exacerbates these changes. The risk of fracturing your bones increases, and your bones also slowly lose their ability to protect your internal organs. Postmenopausal women are particularly at risk because their levels of oestrogen reduce to a point where it is unable to inhibit the action of osteoclasts, resulting in increased bone reabsorption.

The cartilage that coats the ends of your long bones is also vulnerable to the ageing process, given its low background rates of cell division. Around half of the chondrocytes that maintain the cartilage matrix are lost between the ages of 40 and 80 years, increasing the likelihood of arthritic disorders.

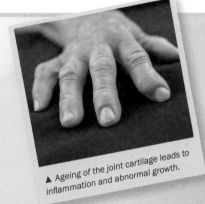

▲ Ageing of the joint cartilage leads to inflammation and abnormal growth.

Ageing also causes deficits in your proprioceptive ability, which is your sense of position and orientation. This arises when the stretch receptors in your ligaments decrease in number, compromising the awareness of where your joints are in space.

AGEING MUSCLES

Sarcopenia is a term used to describe the loss of skeletal muscle mass and its ability to function properly. This progressive age-related syndrome comes with its own set of drawbacks, such as reduced quality of life and increased risk of disability and death.

Loss of muscle mass arises when the myofibrils within myofibres waste away, reducing its overall thickness, which is more pronounced in the fast type 2 myofibres. The pace at which this arises is quite shocking. Your myofibrils atrophy at a rate of about 3 to 8 per cent every decade from the age of 30 years, with the rate increasing over the age of 65. Muscle loss is also associated with a decrease in the number of myofibres: between the ages of 24 and 50 years, the rate of decline speeds up from 5 to 35 per cent. It is thought that age-related changes to the neuromuscular junction cause the associated neuron to detach (denervate) from the myofibre, which then dies by apoptosis (see page 52). Satellite cells that normally regenerate damaged muscle are not spared either, and their population declines with age by as much as 50 per cent.

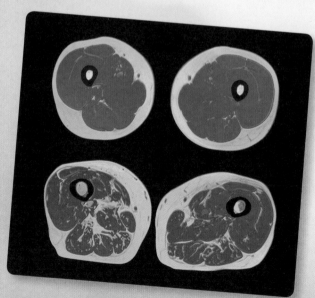

◀ These MRI scans show the thighs of a healthy 31-year-old man (top) and a healthy 81-year-old man (bottom). The loss of muscle mass and increase in fibrofatty tissue typifies the effects of sarcopenia.

The type of myofibres lost also affects the ability of your muscles to work properly. Ageing appears to cause the loss of motor neurons that innervate the fast type 2 myofibres. Not only does this reduce their numbers, but also results in some being reinnervated by slow type 2 motor neurons, which changes their response times, load-bearing capacity, co-ordination and strength.

The muscle architecture also gets disturbed by increased amounts of fibrofatty tissue. This adds to a plethora

▲ *Dancing is believed to be a fun way to slow down or reverse the rate of skeletal muscle loss and also improve brain health in the elderly.*

of age-related changes that affect the muscle–bone relationship dynamic, and ultimately reduces the ability of exercise to increase your strength and bone mass. However, it seems the adage 'Use it or lose it' holds true, because evidence suggests that the rate of muscle loss could be offset by regular exercise, especially in the form of dance.

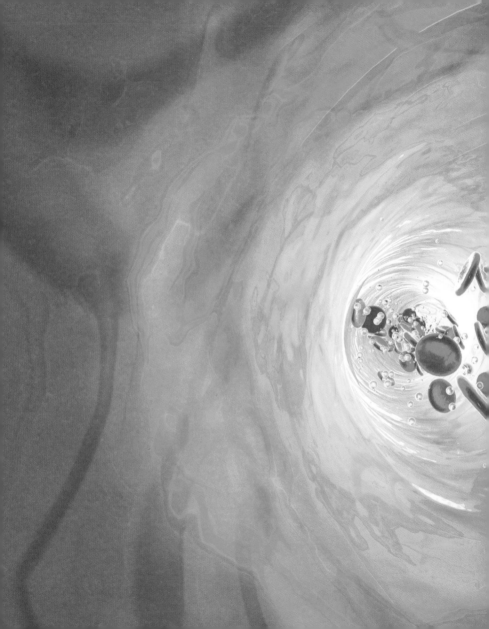

CHAPTER 5

A BLOOD RED SUPERHIGHWAY

THE CARDIOVASCULAR SYSTEM

Every ordered entity knows that things must flow for the system to work. Without the flow, everything festers and becomes stagnant. Your cardiovascular system knows this and has built its very existence upon it.

By keeping your blood flowing, your cardiovascular system provides the ultimate transport service: it allows every cell in your body to receive the life-giving gas oxygen and an assortment of life-sustaining nutrients, plus security protection. Your cardiovascular system also acts as a fluid-based mode of communication for hormones that travel from their base organ to their target cells. If that were not enough, it moonshines as a waste disposal carrier for carbon dioxide and other substances your body either no longer wants or must remove. This workaholic system also supports other systems by helping them maintain the composition of your blood and ensuring homeostasis.

▶ *The cardiovascular system is a closed system that flows in one direction only.*

CARDIOVASCULAR SYSTEM

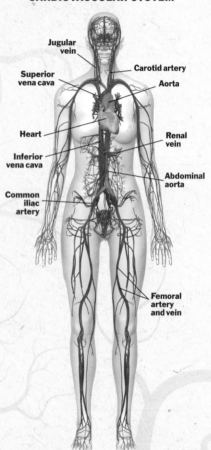

- Jugular vein
- Carotid artery
- Superior vena cava
- Aorta
- Heart
- Renal vein
- Inferior vena cava
- Abdominal aorta
- Common iliac artery
- Femoral artery and vein

INVOLUNTARY MUSCLES

Two types of muscle tissue have evolved to help your body systems move without your conscious control. Aside from the arrector pili muscle of the skin, they form the walls of some of your internal organs and hollow tubes.

Cardiac muscle: Along with skeletal muscle (see pages 96–99), cardiac muscle is striated, or marked with dark and light bands. This arises from actomyosin filaments that are parallel to each other, forming structural units called sarcomeres. Unlike skeletal muscle, cardiac muscle creates its own stimulus to contract without cerebral input. Cardiac muscle fibres branch out to each other, helping electrical signals spread quickly to neighbouring cells. Cardiac muscle is only found in your heart.

Smooth muscle: This type of muscle is found throughout your body, either in organs that require hollow tubes to constrict, or where muscles pull structures without your conscious control, as in your eyes or skin. These long tapering muscle cells cause slow wave-like movements that allow them to work for long periods without fatigue. In your cardiovascular system, they line the walls of your blood vessels, some of which constrict to help push blood around your body.

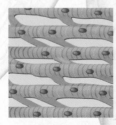

▲ Cardiac muscle

▲ Skeletal muscle

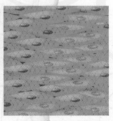

▲ Smooth muscle

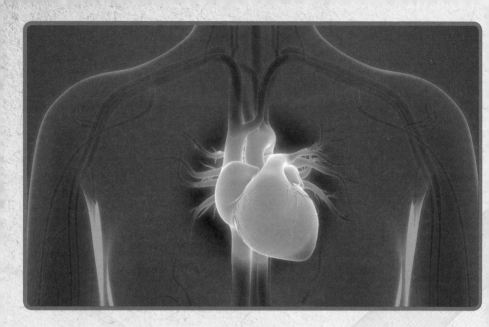

HEART OF THE MATTER

The ancient Egyptians were the first civilization to document that the heart was at the centre of many body processes. While they correctly recognized its special relationship with your lungs and blood, their spiritual and religious beliefs led them to think that the heart was the source of all your thoughts and emotions, including your intelligence. The dichotomy one faces while having to base a decision on one's head or heart might indeed be a real one, because your heart and brain work together to influence how you feel. The heart is more than just a mechanical structure or pump: it contains its own source of specialized neurons, which, some could argue, suggests it has an intelligence of its own.

Composed entirely of muscle, your heart is about the size of your fist. It is often assumed to reside on the left side of your body, but it straddles the midline and tilts slightly to the left. Roughly a rounded triangle, it is tucked between your lungs, anterior to (in front of) the spine and posterior to (behind) the chest bone, with its point lying just below your left nipple.

This pumping maniac of an organ requires more oxygen than any other muscle in your body. To ensure this happens, it has procured its own separate blood supply in the form of coronary arteries. This enables it to pump around 7,500l (15,850 pints) of your blood daily.

Your blood collects oxygen from your lungs and nutrients from your digestive system, then charters them to your entire body before it makes a return journey back to the heart, carrying waste products in its cargo. The process by which this occurs is highly choreographed and uses a network of vessels that brings blood to your heart (veins) or takes blood away from your heart (arteries).

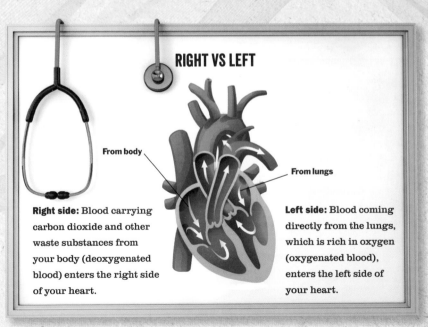

RIGHT VS LEFT

From body

From lungs

Right side: Blood carrying carbon dioxide and other waste substances from your body (deoxygenated blood) enters the right side of your heart.

Left side: Blood coming directly from the lungs, which is rich in oxygen (oxygenated blood), enters the left side of your heart.

WALLS OF THE HEART

Broadly speaking, there are three main walls of your heart. The outer wall, or pericardium, and inner wall, called the endocardium, are made of thin connective tissue. The pericardium's job is to protect the heart from its constant contractions. The endocardium provides a smooth surface for blood to flow freely to prevent clotting. In between these layers is the main tissue, or myocardium. This thick cardiac muscle is made up of cells that connect to each other through branches.

CHAMBERS OF THE HEART

There are four chambers that collect and pump blood in stages. The walls of these muscular bags contract in a coordinated fashion to push your blood forward in one direction. These chambers are divided into two different types, atria and ventricles, and both sides of your heart, left and right, have one of each.

Atria: These form the upper chambers and receive blood entering your heart. Their walls are relatively thin compared to ventricles. They pump blood into the ventricles. The left atrium is separated from the right atrium by a thin part of the wall, or septum, called the interatrial septum.

Ventricles: These lower chambers are the main pumps. Their walls are thicker because they push blood out of the heart. Blood is pumped out either to the lungs (right side, deoxygenated) or to the rest of the body (left side, oxygenated). The left ventricle is thicker than the right because it does more work and pumps against greater pressure, so high it would squirt blood about 10m (33ft) into the air. The interventricular septum separates the left and right ventricles.

VALVES

These fibrous tissues help ensure that the blood flows in one direction. They separate the upper and lower chambers on each side via the atrioventricular valves and form the semilunar valves in the large vessels of the heart. Together with the septa they ensure segregation of deoxygenated and oxygenated blood, for absolutely no mixing is allowed.

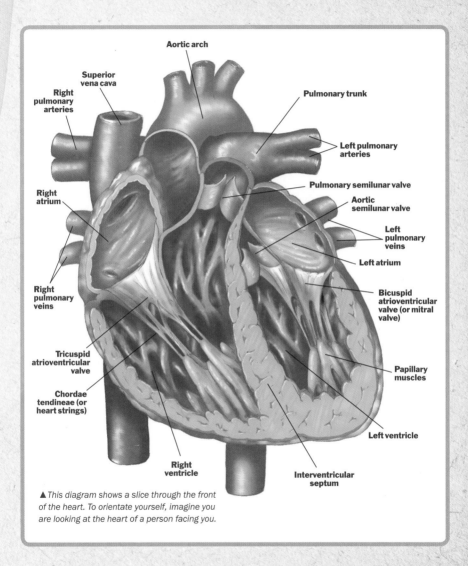

Aortic arch

Superior vena cava

Right pulmonary arteries

Pulmonary trunk

Left pulmonary arteries

Pulmonary semilunar valve

Aortic semilunar valve

Right atrium

Left pulmonary veins

Left atrium

Right pulmonary veins

Bicuspid atrioventricular valve (or mitral valve)

Tricuspid atrioventricular valve

Papillary muscles

Chordae tendineae (or heart strings)

Left ventricle

Right ventricle

Interventricular septum

▲ This diagram shows a slice through the front of the heart. To orientate yourself, imagine you are looking at the heart of a person facing you.

AND THE BEAT GOES...BUMPTY BUMP

Your heart beats about 42 million times every year. This figure assumes you have a resting heart rate of 80 beats per minute (bpm), but it can be anywhere between 60 and 100 in a healthy adult. Each beat ejects about 70ml (2½fl oz) of blood into your system, equivalent to about 5l (10½ pints) every minute, which increases six-fold when you exercise.

The science of the heartbeat is a work of art. A choreographed and controlled sequence of events allows the two atria to contract in unison and fill the ventricles with blood. As the atria relax, the ventricles contract and expel 50 to 70 per cent of the blood they acquire, before they take their break, momentarily, and then the cycle repeats itself.

ELECTRICAL IMPULSES

The cycle begins with the sinoatrial node, a special patch of heart muscle comprising nerve cells equipped with the ability to generate an electrical impulse without any input from your brain. Situated in the upper right atrium, this mother of all pacemakers fires at regular intervals across the atria, causing them to contract. As the impulse

flows through the heart, it reaches an impasse known as the atrioventricular node (AVN). At this junction between the atria and ventricles, unrestricted access is not permitted. To reach the ventricles, the impulse must pass through a team of connecting fibres called the 'bundle of His' before it can spread out and impose itself upon the ventricular mass. This clever diversion stops the impulse reaching the ventricles at the same time as the atria, causing the ventricles to contract about 100 milliseconds later.

Your heart is not totally independent from your brain. It needs neural input for guidance, to tell it when to speed up or slow down. This occurs through the sympathetic and parasympathetic nerves of your autonomic nervous system (see pages 216–19).

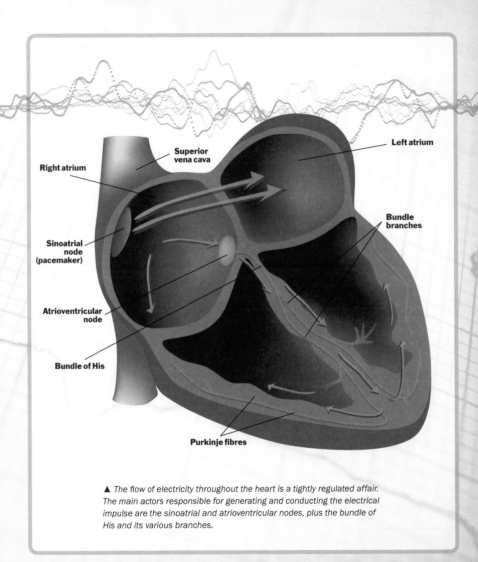

Superior
vena cava

Left atrium

Right atrium

Bundle
branches

Sinoatrial
node
(pacemaker)

Atrioventricular
node

Bundle of His

Purkinje fibres

▲ The flow of electricity throughout the heart is a tightly regulated affair.
The main actors responsible for generating and conducting the electrical
impulse are the sinoatrial and atrioventricular nodes, plus the bundle of
His and its various branches.

THE CARDIAC CYCLE

In a single heartbeat, your heart exists in two distinct states: diastole, when your chambers are relaxed, and systole, when your chambers contract.

Diastole: During atrial diastole, the right atrium fills with deoxygenated blood from the vena cava, while the left atrium fills with oxygenated blood from the pulmonary vein.

Systole: During ventricular systole, the pressure build-up forces the atrioventricular valves to close and the semilunar valves to open. Deoxygenated blood in the right ventricle passes into the pulmonary artery through the pulmonary semilunar valve

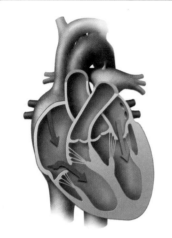

▲ Diastole (heart filling)

PHASE	HEART	ATRIA	VENTRICLES	ATRIOVENTRICULAR VALVES	SEMILUNAR VALVES
Diastole	Both chambers relaxed	Fill with blood	Fill with blood (passive flow from atria)	Open	Closed
Systole	Atria contract, ventricles relaxed	Empty themselves of blood	Fill with more blood (pressure increases)	Open	Closed
	Ventricles contract, atria relaxed	Relax	Empty themselves of most of the blood	Closed	Open

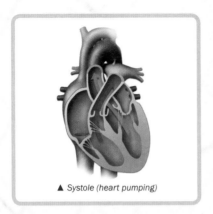
▲ *Systole (heart pumping)*

for distribution to your lungs, while oxygenated blood in the left ventricle passes into the aorta through the aortic semilunar valve for distribution to the rest of your body. The opening and closing of these valves produce the characteristic lub-dub sound. At the end of the contraction, the ventricles enter diastole for some much-needed downtime.

SEE THE HEARTBEAT

An electrocardiogram (ECG) is a recording of the electrical impulses that occur while your heart beats. Sensors that detect the electrical signals are attached to the skin overlying your heart and connected to an ECG recording machine, which produces a tracing of your heart's electrical activity. The readout shows different stages of the cardiac cycle that appear as characteristic waves of electrical activity, each with their own unique shape. The shape of the trace can be used to determine whether the heart is beating normally or abnormally.

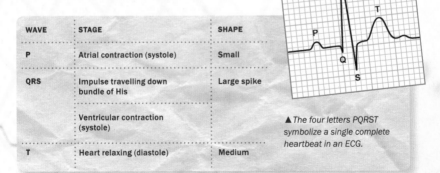

WAVE	STAGE	SHAPE
P	Atrial contraction (systole)	Small
QRS	Impulse travelling down bundle of His	Large spike
	Ventricular contraction (systole)	
T	Heart relaxing (diastole)	Medium

▲ *The four letters PQRST symbolize a single complete heartbeat in an ECG.*

▶ Arteries and veins differ in the thickness of their walls and the size of their lumen.

Tunica externa

Tunica media

Tunica intima

Artery

Lumen

Vein

TRANSPORT NETWORK

Your body houses an extensive network of blood vessels that branch out into ever-decreasing sizes and transport vital nutrients to all parts of your body. The network is so vast that, if it were unravelled and stretched out end to end, it would reach around the entire globe at least two and a half times.

Aside from adding to your framework and bulk, and providing routes along which blood travels, this root-like system also uses tiny vessels close to the skin to regulate your temperature. It does this by constricting blood vessels to conserve heat and relaxing them to release heat. This is possible because most of your blood vessels have muscles in their walls.

TYPES OF BLOOD VESSELS

There are two main 'camps' to which your blood vessels belong: those in camp A are part of the arterial system and their role is to carry blood away from your heart to your tissues. To be a member, one needs a thick elasticated and muscular skin capable of withstanding the great pressures exerted by the heart and to help propel the blood forward. Those in camp V belong to the venous system and their role is to collect and carry blood to the heart. These blood vessels are leaner because they endure less pressure and have valves to help ensure they keep the blood flowing in one direction.

There is a lesser, third type (in terms of size) but its role is far from inferior. Capillaries act as a 'go between'

between the two camps and facilitate the exchange of materials between your blood and your tissues. These tiny, often unappreciated vessels are the ones that come into close contact with every cell in your body and form their own capillary community in the process.

BLOOD VESSEL STRUCTURE

All blood vessels, except capillaries, have the same basic structure:

Tunica externa: Each is covered in an outer sheath of connective tissue called the tunica externa or adventitia.

Tunica media: The middle sheath is where smooth muscles and elastic fibres equip the vessel with motility and elastic skills.

Tunica intima: The innermost sheath comprises a single smooth layer of flattened endothelial cells.

Lumen: The central space through which blood flows is the lumen.

CAPILLARIES

Capillaries are made of only a single layer of endothelial cells, covered with a very thin membrane and with a diameter as wide as a single red blood cell. Muscles have plenty of capillaries because they need constant feeding. Capillaries are so thin that substances are easily exchanged between your blood and tissue fluid. A network or capillary bed forms around the tissue and this connects the arterial system to your body's drainage system – the veins.

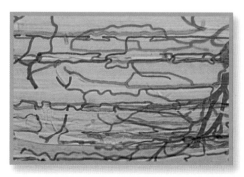

◄▲ Capillaries are the tiniest blood vessels. They comprise the tunica intima layer only.

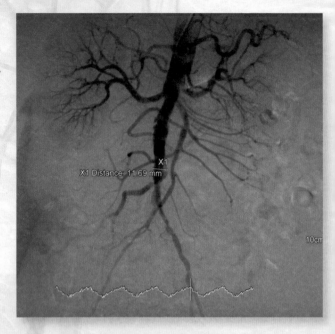

► *Your blood vessels can be visualized using a special type of X-ray called an angiogram.*

X1
X1 Distance - 11.69 mm

10cm

ARTERIAL SYSTEM

The term artery comes from the Greek word '*arteria*' which means air in a vessel. Ancient Greeks gave them this moniker because they believed arteries carried nothing but air. This was based on their observation that these vessels were always devoid of any blood after death, which we now know is due to blood accumulating in the veins after the heart stops beating.

Arteries do carry the air we breathe, but not in the literal sense. All bar one of them transport oxygenated blood away from your heart; the pulmonary artery, however, takes deoxygenated blood away from your heart to your lungs, where it gets oxygenated and returns.

Aorta: All arteries stem from two sources: the aorta and pulmonary artery. The size of a hosepipe, the aorta is the largest artery in your body and originates from the left ventricle of your heart. Upon leaving, it forms an arch from which spring forth antler-like arteries that nourish structures in your head and arms. Like an upside-down 'U' it doubles back on itself to descend toward your chest, abdomen and lower regions, with further branches arising.

▶ *Your arterial system emanates from two main arteries, the aorta and pulmonary trunk, which both sprout directly from your heart.*

Coronary arteries: Prior to its U-turn, the aorta first ensures it provides the heart with its own blood supply in the form of the coronary arteries that subdivide into a network of smaller vessels. The heart needs this because the myocardium and pericardium are too far away to receive the nutrients in the blood that nourish the inner endocardium.

Pulmonary arteries: Pulmonary arteries, which supply the lungs with blood, are much shorter than their systemic counterparts and begin at the base of the right ventricle, before splitting into left and right divisions.

Arterioles: Arterioles are the smallest arteries in your arterial system and are the vessels from which capillaries arise. They deliver and regulate blood flow to the capillary network by recruiting a band of circular smooth muscle fibres called precapillary sphincters. These muscular ribs constrict at the brain's command to reduce the arterioles' diameter and thus the subsequent blood flow to the capillaries. For this reason, arterioles are also referred to as precapillary resistance vessels.

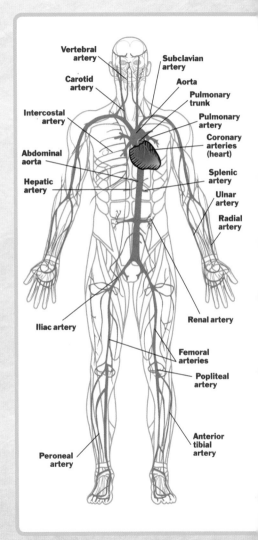

Vertebral artery
Subclavian artery
Carotid artery
Aorta
Pulmonary trunk
Intercostal artery
Pulmonary artery
Coronary arteries (heart)
Abdominal aorta
Hepatic artery
Splenic artery
Ulnar artery
Radial artery
Renal artery
Iliac artery
Femoral arteries
Popliteal artery
Anterior tibial artery
Peroneal artery

THE VENOUS SYSTEM

The smallest veins are the venules. These crawl out from the capillary bed and converge into increasingly larger veins, some of which have flap extensions of their wall called valves. In between heartbeats, the pressure in your system falls and blood temporarily moves backward, which forces the valves shut and prevents backflow. Compared to arteries, veins have a wider lumen and thinner walls containing less elastic tissue and smooth muscle. Their lack of bulk arises because the pressure exerted by the heart in the arteries dissipates by the time blood reaches the venous system.

Wherever there is an artery, you will find a vein that transports the deoxygenated blood back to the heart. Veins from your head, arms and neck converge at the superior vena cava, while veins draining your torso and legs converge at the inferior vena cava. Both these veins enter the right atrium, as does the coronary sinus, a structure formed by the merging of coronary veins that drain the heart itself of deoxygenated blood. The veins that drain your lungs converge into the pulmonary vein, which – unlike any other vein – carries oxygen rich blood to the left atrium.

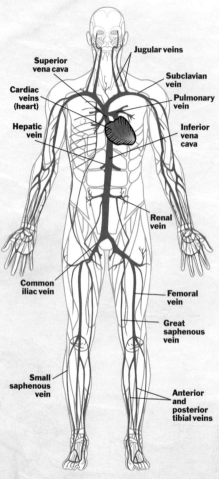

▲ About 60 per cent of your blood volume gathers in your veins, which all converge into either the vena cava or pulmonary vein before entering your heart.

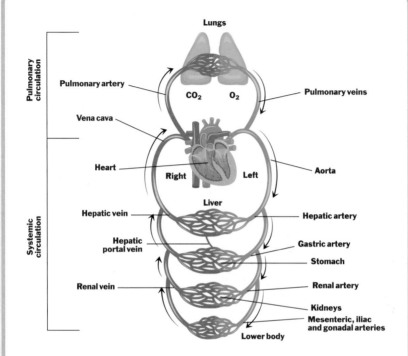

Lungs

Pulmonary circulation

Pulmonary artery — CO_2 O_2 — Pulmonary veins

Vena cava — Pulmonary veins

Heart — Aorta

Right Left

Liver

Hepatic vein — Hepatic artery

Hepatic portal vein — Gastric artery

Stomach

Renal vein — Renal artery

Kidneys

Mesenteric, iliac and gonadal arteries

Lower body

Systemic circulation

DUAL CIRCULATION

There are two separate circulations that yoke with each other.

The systemic circulation pumps oxygenated blood from the left ventricle via the aorta to every part of your body, except your lungs.

The lungs have their own pulmonary circulation. The deoxygenated blood from your tissues enters the right atrium via the vena cavas, then enters the right ventricle and is pumped out via the pulmonary artery to your lungs, where it dumps carbon dioxide and becomes oxygenated and travels back via the pulmonary veins to the left atrium, before going into the left ventricle and restarting the circuit.

THE RED STUFF

British historian and biographer Robert Lacey explains in his book *Aristocrats* that it was the Spaniards who first brought to the world's consciousness the idea that an aristocrat's blood was blue. This harks back to the European Middle Ages, when an individual's class was commonly ranked based on the visibility of their superficial blue veins. Those of an elevated status had paler skin and thus more prominent blue veins compared to their more tanned peasant counterparts, who worked in the fields.

▲ Arctic ice fish are see-through because their clear blood does not contain any red blood cells.

If you have pale skin, the reason your veins appear blue is down to the physics of electromagnetic radiation or, more specifically, the behaviour of different wavelengths of light as they penetrate your skin. Red and orange light have much longer wavelengths and so get absorbed by your skin and the haemoglobin in your blood. With its much shorter wavelength, blue light does not penetrate as deep and reflects back to your eyes, making you see blue.

Apart from horseshoe crabs or ocellated icefish, most vertebrates have red blood. Its exact shade depends on how much oxygen and carbon dioxide it contains. Oxygenated blood is typically bright crimson red, while deoxygenated blood is

▲ *Your blood is a type of liquid connective tissue that teems with cells that help keep you alive.*

more of a dark maroon red, both of which are determined by the protein pigment haemoglobin in your red blood cells.

Your entire cardiovascular system holds about 5l (10½ pints) of blood. You can withstand losing about a quarter of this volume without suffering any long-term adverse effects, which is why donations are possible.

MAKE-UP OF BLOOD

Blood is teeming with cells that flow in its current. Red blood cells occupy most of this habitat (45 per cent), followed by white blood cells (1 per cent) and tiny clotting fragments called platelets. Each of these cell types emigrated here from outside the vessel and play a vital role in keeping you alive. A pale-yellow fluid called plasma makes up the remaining volume of blood (54 per cent). Mostly water, it provides the perfect solute for various essential substances to dissolve and suspend themselves.

Without your blood, your body would be unable to seal breaks in the system and prevent harmful invaders from entering. There would be no ability to engage an emergency response team; nor would there be any mechanism to transport the foot soldiers of your immune system to tackle those that made it through. Clearly, blood serves a fundamental role in your defence, and for this reason white blood cells and platelets are discussed further in Chapter 6 (see pages 148–55 and 160).

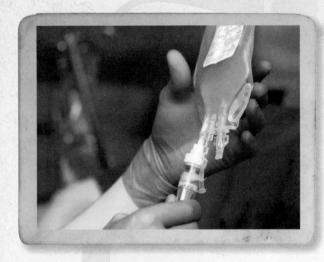

◀ Blood plasma contains many important substances, including clotting factors and immunoglobulins.

PLASMA

Question 1: What would be left if you removed all the blood cells from blood? The answer is: plasma. Blood plasma looks a bit like your pee concentrated, but unlike urine it contains things that your body does not necessarily want to throw out. It is 90 per cent water and includes nutrients such as glucose, the building blocks of fats and proteins (i.e. fatty acids and amino acids), cholesterol, hormones, iron, vitamins, minerals, dissolved salts or electrolytes (e.g. sodium and potassium), cellular waste products, urea and various globular proteins that have a variety of roles, including working as enzymes or providing a river taxi service for some of the more water-hating substances.

The most abundant protein in your blood is albumin. It is made in the liver and enters the blood to perform an extremely vital role. Albumin binds to various hydrophobic molecules in the blood, such as hormones, steroids and fatty acids, including drugs, and helps distribute them within your body fluids. It also acts as a circulating sponge to prevent water from diffusing out of the vessels. By providing the necessary osmotic pressure required to keep water in your blood, albumin prevents your tissues from oversoaking.

Globulins are another important blood plasma protein that originate either in the liver or white blood cells. They perform similar carrier services as albumin for various substances, and also serve as clotting factors, such as fibrinogen, to prevent blood loss. However, one function that only a brave type of globulin, the immunoglobulins, takes on is to be an antibody, which forms part of your armoury against invading pathogens.

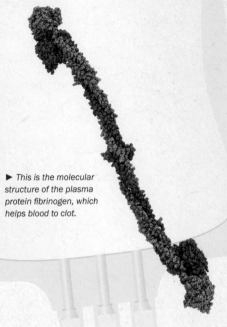

► This is the molecular structure of the plasma protein fibrinogen, which helps blood to clot.

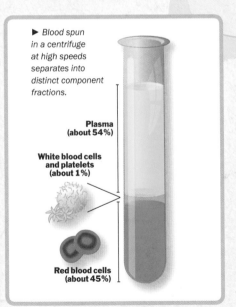

► Blood spun in a centrifuge at high speeds separates into distinct component fractions.

Plasma
(about 54%)

White blood cells and platelets
(about 1%)

Red blood cells
(about 45%)

SERUM

Question 2: What do you get if you take away clotting factors such as fibrinogen from plasma? The answer is: serum. This is the part of your blood that doctors use to test for various diseases or to determine your blood group. Plasma, however, is used in blood transfusions for individuals whose blood cannot clot (haemophiliacs), or who require a top-up of specific immunoglobins because their immune system is compromised.

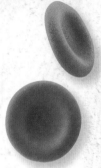

Red blood cells, or erythrocytes, begin life in your bone marrow within the spaces of the cancellous spongy bone. During the first three months of your life after conception, your liver and spleen had the responsibility of producing erythrocytes. After completing a mandatory stint in the womb, and subsequent restructuring, the role was transferred to your bone marrow, relegating your liver and spleen to reserve position on the off-chance your marrow fails.

RED BLOOD CELLS: LIFE AND TIMES OF AN OXYGEN CARRIER

▼ These are the different stages of red blood cell formation (erythropoiesis). Once a stem cell (top left) is committed to producing an erythrocyte it undergoes a series of morphological changes, which ultimately result in the cell losing its nucleus (bottom right) and organelles and acquiring the pigment haemoglobin.

After birth, all your bones, especially the long ones, were initially capable of producing erythrocytes in a process known as erythropoiesis. By your early twenties, this ability is restricted to a chosen few, namely your backbone,

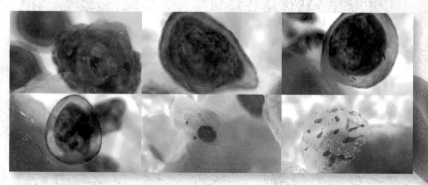

breastbone, cranium, pelvic bone and the proximal ends of your limb bones.

ERYTHROPOIESIS

The whole process of erythropoiesis starts when certain cells in your kidneys detect low levels of oxygen in your blood. They release a hormone, or growth factor, called erythropoietin that stimulates the division of haematopoietic stem cells called haemocytoblasts that live in your bone marrow. These are the cells from which all blood cells originate.

A subsequent daughter cell differentiates into a myeloid stem cell that gives rise to early precursor versions of red blood cells called proerythroblasts. After a series of further changes, the cell gradually loses it nucleus and migrates into your blood, where it becomes a young erythrocyte known as a reticulocyte.

Haematopoiesis is the name for the overarching process of producing all types of blood cells, which all form by a process similar to that of erythrocytes.

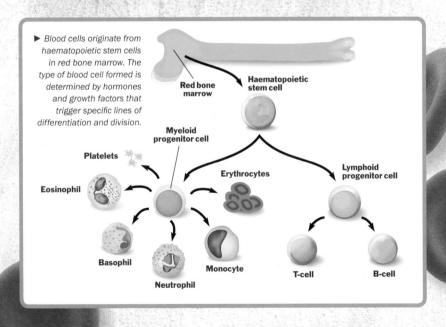

▶ Blood cells originate from haematopoietic stem cells in red bone marrow. The type of blood cell formed is determined by hormones and growth factors that trigger specific lines of differentiation and division.

Red bone marrow

Haematopoietic stem cell

Myeloid progenitor cell

Platelets

Eosinophil

Erythrocytes

Lymphoid progenitor cell

Basophil

Monocyte

Neutrophil

T-cell

B-cell

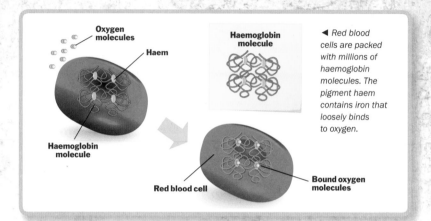

Oxygen molecules

Haem

Haemoglobin molecule

Red blood cell

Haemoglobin molecule

Bound oxygen molecules

◀ *Red blood cells are packed with millions of haemoglobin molecules. The pigment haem contains iron that loosely binds to oxygen.*

CARRYING OXYGEN

Reticulocytes, or immature erythrocytes, represent 1–2 per cent of red blood cells in your circulation. Within two days, a reticulocyte trades in all its organelles for space, to pack into its frame its most prized possession, haemoglobin. At this point, we can call this mature cell an erythrocyte.

The reason your blood tastes like metal is because each haemoglobin molecule has four iron-containing pigments called haem that are each wrapped by four globulin protein chains. The iron exists in a form that reversibly binds to oxygen (ferrous iron, Fe^{2+}), so a single haemoglobin molecule will bind to four oxygen molecules. This may

not sound like much, but consider that each individual erythrocyte contains up to 300 million haemoglobin molecules, which means that each single red blood cell can bind to and transport up to 1.2 billion oxygen molecules. Now consider that there are about 30 trillion blood cells in your circulation.

The free-floating erythrocytes, which are essentially haemoglobin molecules packed in a membrane, adopt a biconcave shape to increase the surface area for gaseous exchange. Interestingly, haemoglobin only ever releases its oxygen if a tissue needs it. Furthermore, only about one-quarter of the carbon dioxide waste produced from your tissues binds to protein areas in the haemoglobin molecule: most dissolve and travel to your lungs in the plasma.

DEATH OF AN ERYTHROCYTE

After about 120 days, your oxygen-carrier erythrocyte reaches old age. Those that are no longer viable are recognized by specialized white blood cells called macrophages that engulf and destroy them back in their place of origin, in the bone marrow, liver and spleen. However, this is not the end. During this process, component parts of the red blood cell – the globin proteins and iron – are recycled and donated to make more red blood cells. Other parts, such as the haem, are converted to pigments that first start off green (biliverdin) before becoming the yellow substance bilirubin, which piggybacks a ride on albumin in the blood to go straight to the liver. Once there, it is upcycled to make the digestive fluid bile, which breaks down fats in your intestines.

The life of a red blood cell is relatively short, but with new erythrocytes produced in your bone marrow at the rate of about 2 million every second, its legacy continues on, and on.

▶ *At the end of its life, a red blood cell is recognized and eaten by a phagocytic cell (macrophage). Its component parts are either recycled to produce new cells or excreted in bile as the pigment bilirubin.*

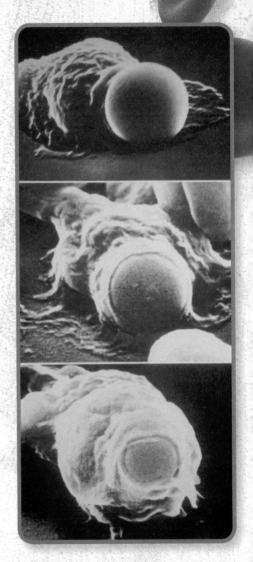

UNDER PRESSURE

Can you feel your blood pulsing through your arteries? If you can, you probably should get your blood pressure checked. Your heart is no softy. It can push blood at rather high pressure, so high, in fact, that your blood would easily scale the height of three adult brown bears standing on top of each other. Blood pressure is a measure of how hard your heart pushes blood against the walls of your arteries.

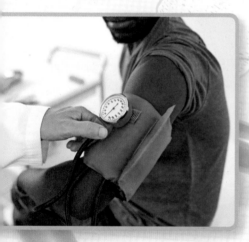

▲ Blood pressure is typically monitored using a sphygmomanometer.

Since your blood flows through your arteries in pulses, the pressure it exerts on the arterial wall varies, which makes getting an accurate reading all the more challenging. The best approach is to take an average of the highest and lowest pressures your arteries endure. Since your left ventricle does the lion's share of work (to ensure your systemic circulation gets its supplies) the highest arterial, or systolic, pressure arises during contraction of your left ventricle (systole) when blood is being pumped out of the aorta. The lowest arterial, or diastolic, pressure arises when the heart has stopped contracting and is completely relaxed at the end of diastole. Blood pressure is then expressed as systolic/diastolic and measured in millimeters of mercury (mmHg) using a

manual blood pressure monitor called a
sphygmomanometer. Digital versions also exist.

HIGHER OR LOWER

When it comes to blood pressure,
there is no such thing as normal.
It varies according to your
genetics, age and activity
levels. Blood pressure
temporarily rises during
exercise and decreases
when you rest. The
systolic pressure of a
one-year-old baby is
around 90 mmHg and
this increases to around
105 mmHg by the time
a child reaches 10 years
of age. A typical reading in
a healthy resting adult would
be 120 mmHg (systolic)/80 mmHg
(diastolic). However, your blood pressure
would have to climb to at least 140/90 for you to be
diagnosed with hypertension – or 160/90 if you are elderly because age tends to stiffen
the major arteries and cause the systolic pressure to rise. Of course, it can also go the
other way too. A reading of less than 90/60 generally indicates that you have low blood
pressure or hypotension.

Too high or too low is bad news. Sustained hypertension is the cause of many
serious and life-threatening diseases, such as stroke, heart disease, aneurysms (where
your blood vessel bulges and is at risk of rupturing), sleep disorders, dementia, vision
impairment and kidney disease. Hypotension often indicates that your brain and other
organs are not getting enough blood, which can have various causes and lead to a
range of symptoms, such as dizziness, fainting and palpitations.

YOUR PULSE

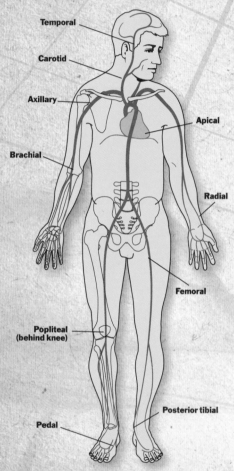

Temporal

Carotid

Axillary

Apical

Brachial

Radial

Femoral

Popliteal
(behind knee)

Posterior tibial

Pedal

▲ *The carotid pulse is one of the strongest
pulse points in your body.*

'There is music wherever there is rhythm, as there is life wherever there beats a pulse,' said Igor Stravinsky (1882–1971). Indeed, music and the pulse are inextricably linked. From an evolutionary perspective, the whole purpose of music is to modulate your state of being. Its tempo can influence your pulse rate, effectively tuning your heartbeat.

At 60 beats per minute (bpm), a ticking clock can soothe, as your pulse rate attempts to synchronize with the slow tempo of the tick-tock. Just as the cadence of relaxing music can help slow your heartbeat, fast music supports high-energy activities like exercise and dance.

Your pulse and heart rate are united through the kinetic energy generated by contraction of your left ventricle. Like waves across the sea, this expanding and recoiling force is transmitted along the walls of your arteries and comes alive at areas where the waves meet a firm or bony surface, or where they simply lie close enough to kiss the skin. Proximity to the heart determines their strength, the closest producing the strongest pulse and those furthest away the weakest.

FINDING THE PULSE

The pulse that gives the most accurate measurements arises on the inner surface of the wrist just below the thumb. Known as the radial pulse, it requires the use of two fingers but no thumb, because that has a pulse of its own. The carotid pulse in the neck is often used if the radial pulse is hidden in an obese patient. Other pulses can be found in your temple, arm, groin, back of knee, inside of your ankle and top of your foot.

PULSE RATES

The strength, rhythm and rate of your pulse can provide useful information about your general state of health. Pulse rates naturally vary according to your age, fitness and body temperature, and whether you are feeling anxious or ill. Resting rates above 100 bpm are generally considered abnormal and are known as tachycardia. Equally unusual are rates below 50 bpm, which are known as bradycardia. A faint or weak pulse is always a cause for concern and often constitutes a medical emergency as it indicates that your heart is pumping only a small volume of blood, or that there is a potential blockage in the system. If the pattern at which the beats occur is irregular, this suggests that your heart chambers are not moving in a coordinated fashion but rather dancing to the beat of their own drum in a heightened state known as arrhythmia.

▶ *Taking the radial pulse involves palpating the radial artery with your fingers (not thumb).*

TOO MUCH EXERCISE?

The connection between moderate exercise and improved cardiovascular health has long been established. Armoured with the proverbial green light from your primary care physician, all it takes is about 20 minutes of gentle aerobic exercise every day at a level capable of raising your heartbeat above its resting rate to help you fight against high blood pressure and the ravages of diseases, such as arteriosclerosis (where the walls of your arteries harden), stroke and heart attacks. However, the balance between good cardiovascular health and exercise gets trickier as the level of exercise increases.

▼ The cardiovascular system of endurance athletes is conditioned to endure intense levels of exercise. This leads to physiological adaptive changes which, depending on the individual, may or may not be beneficial.

INTENSE REGIMES

The relationship between exercise and cardiovascular health becomes somewhat tenuous and unpredictable when that exercise requires you to train intensely for very long periods of time. Endurance athletes are known to take their bodies to physiological places very few people can withstand. A combination of the right genetics and extensive training mixed with competitive spirit, sheer grit, willpower and determination provides the necessary cocktail of traits required to endure these extremes.

However, some studies even go as far as to suggest that chronic exposure to intense regimes may be anything but beneficial. Fears about high-dose physical activity and possible adverse cardiovascular outcomes abound, with particular concern over early-onset arrhythmias (atrial fibrillation), undiagnosed changes to the myocardium (cardiomyopathy) and coronary artery disease. Such views have been heavily criticized, as scientific opinions differ.

GETTING THE GREEN LIGHT

What is undisputed, is that the heart remodels itself and undergoes distinct changes at these intense levels of exercise, most of which tend to boost an athlete's performance. However, the implicit assumption is that not all do. For this reason, it becomes vitally important that athletes and highly active people only get the green light after receiving the correct set of assessments that can identify any hidden or unknown vulnerabilities. For example, one such set of standards for diagnosing athletes at risk of complications of the heart has been devised by a group of cardiologists led by Dr Aaron L Baggish, MD and Dr Rory Brett Weiner, MD, assistant professor at Harvard Medical School. They run a clinical programme investigating cardiac performance in competitive athletes at the Massachusetts General Hospital in Boston, USA.

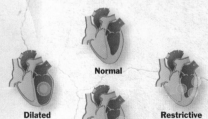

Normal

Dilated

Restrictive

Hypertrophic

◄ Cardiomyopathy (CM) is a blanket term used to describe diseases that arise in the heart muscle. In dilated CM, the walls are stretched, in hypertrophic CM the walls are thickened, while in restrictive CM the walls are stiff.

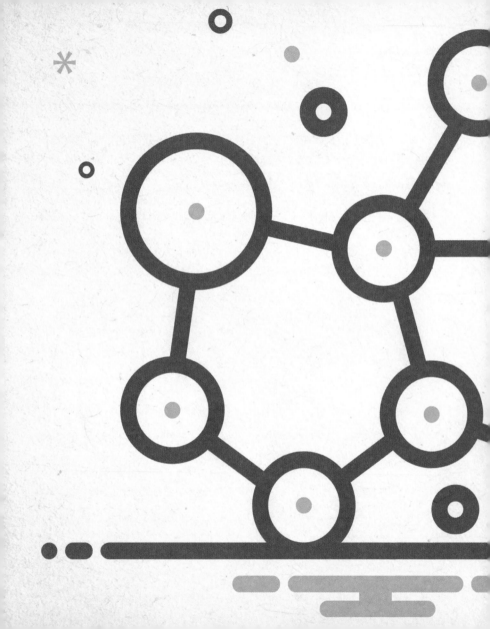

CHAPTER 6

THE SECURITY FORCE

THE LYMPHATIC SYSTEM

Your immune or lymphatic system has its own set of cells, organs and network of vessels to help fight the good fight against microbes that attempt to invade the body. These microbes are smart, with tricks and disguises, constantly learning and evolving and changing their outfits to avoid detection. This is why your body has evolved an equally formidable security force to help protect you.

THE BORDER FORCE

Any competent defence system needs borders, and those borders need protecting. Your body provides this non-specific guard principally in the form of your skin, and also coats your inner cavities with bug-busting slime called mucus. With tightly packed epithelial cells, your skin forms the perfect barricade. Sebaceous glands help by secreting a slightly acidic antibacterial oil coat called the acid mantle, while those friendly bacteria that co-exist on your skin help keep the nasties at bay by producing chemicals to suppress their growth.

ANTIGENS

Antigens are foreign substances, from living and non-living sources, that provoke an immune response. In pathogens, they are usually proteins found on the surface of bacteria, fungi, viruses or other cells. They can also be compounds and foreign particles. Your body will destroy any antigen it does not recognize.

▶ *The sweat produced by a sweat pore can increase the rate of bacterial growth.*

Some microbes try to piggyback their way inside when you breathe and eat by virtue of their existence in the air and on food. Their demise is through entrapment in the mucus lining your airways and digestive system. However, mucus and saliva do not just act like swamps to physically disable: they also contain lysosomes that break down infectious agents (or pathogens) into tiny pieces – a feature also replicated in the tears of your eyes. Still, a fate worse than death befalls microbes that dare enter the stomach: a final bath in a soup of hydrochloric acid.

LYMPHATIC VESSELS AND ORGANS

Any foreign body that manages to overcome these borders has a formidable hurdle to overcome: your lymphatic system. The primary lymphoid organs are the bone marrow and thymus, where immune cells called lymphocytes are produced.

Your 500 or so lymph nodes, along with your spleen, tonsils, appendix and an intestinal bit of tissue called Peyer's patches, are the secondary or peripheral lymphoid organs. They provide the territory for lymphocytes to mature, proliferate and engage with antigens. Lymphatic vessels transport immune cells around the body.

LYMPHATIC SYSTEM

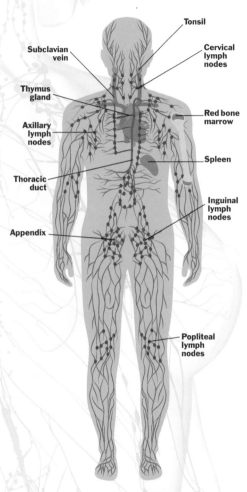

- Tonsil
- Subclavian vein
- Cervical lymph nodes
- Thymus gland
- Red bone marrow
- Axillary lymph nodes
- Spleen
- Thoracic duct
- Inguinal lymph nodes
- Appendix
- Popliteal lymph nodes

▲ The lymphatic system comprises primary and secondary lymphoid organs and lymphatic vessels, of which the thoracic duct is the largest.

TWO IMMUNE DIVISIONS

Your lymphatic system operates under two lines of defence. In the first division, the cells and organs elicit an immediate intrinsic response to any unrecognized agent that dares try to enter your body. Because this instinctive means of attack is deployed irrespective of the invading entity, this response belongs to your innate or non-specific immune system. This is your default system that serves to keep minor pathogens or irritants at bay. Your adaptive immune system is the body's second line of defence.

INNATE IMMUNE SYSTEM

Inflammation is your innate system's main form of defence. It is non-specific to any barrier breach at the local level and results in the release of important molecules called inflammatory mediators. These substances signal and coordinate the recruitment and passage of white blood cells to the affected area and typically result in pain, swelling, heat and redness due to the increased blood flow and collateral damage.

ADAPTIVE IMMUNE SYSTEM

The innate immune system also provides the second division with enough time to fortify and mobilize their resources to deal with emerging threats, which can and do gain access into your circulation.

This acquired and more adaptive immune system comes into force usually several days after the first insult. It is a much-needed time delay because it enables a select group of specialized cells to produce weaponry in the form of cytotoxic chemicals and antibodies capable of targeting specific pathogenic tribes. If the infectious agent has previously trespassed, this response is likely to be much sooner. This is because this autodidactic part of your immune system, which relies heavily on extensive cross-talk, always keeps a record of past threats to elicit a more efficient retaliation in the event of a return attack, thereby building immunity to repeat offenders. It is vital the adaptive immune system gets this right because there is no third line of defence.

Bacteria
(*Streptococcus pneumoniae*)

Fungus
(*Histoplasma*)

Virus
(*Adenoviruses*)

Parasite
(*Ascaris*)

KNOW YOUR ENEMY

Bacteria are everywhere. They are the smallest and yet most abundant life form on Earth. These single-celled organisms, whose ancestors were the first to inhabit this planet, easily outstrip the number of stars in the universe. Their numbers are so vast that it would not be surprising if the current estimates had error margins as large as the estimate itself. It should come as no surprise, therefore, to learn that your body is infested, or rather laden, with trillions of bacteria, most of which live a harmless coexistence on your skin and in your mouth and gut, much to your benefit. However, there are other bacteria that are not so amicable, and they are constantly battling to enter and gain territory in your body and disturb the harmonious utopia within. What is worse: they are not the only ones. Other entities, such as viruses, as well as harmful microbes like parasites and certain fungi, also have this insatiable hunger for cell grab.

◄ *All of these pathogens can cause pneumonia, or inflammation of the lungs. Pathogens are responsible for many of the diseases that afflict humans and animals.*

147

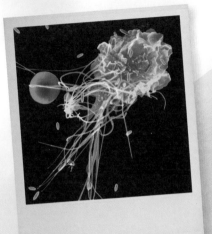

◀ A macrophage presents at the site of bacterial invasion (green). Its dendritic parts help entrap and sample the bacteria and surrounding area.

MYELOID OR LYMPHOID

Myeloid progeny includes red blood cells, platelets and white blood cells called granulocytes and monocytes. Granulocytes and monocytes form most of the leukocytes in the innate immune system. Lymphoid progeny includes a mixture of white blood cells that engage in innate or adaptive immune cell responses: natural killer cells and lymphocytes respectively.

The stimulus to divide arises when the stem cell receives the appropriate signal, or growth factor. Cytokines are complex protein-carbohydrate growth factors released from various cells either in distress or working in defence. They stimulate the production and migration of leukocytes from the various lymphoid organs and tissues. All cells of the blood exist as immature versions principally in the bone marrow, where they take the suffix 'blast'. These mostly migrate to other lymphoid tissues and organs before they activate and fully mature into cells that have the suffix 'cyte'.

WHITE BLOOD CELLS

All white blood cells, also known as leukocytes, begin life in the bone marrow. They all derive from a haematopoietic stem cell called a haemocytoblast in a process called haematopoiesis (see page 133). Being self-renewing stem cells, one daughter cell maintains the stem cell population, while the other becomes an early progenitor form of one of two distinct blood cell dynasties: the myeloid or lymphoid stem cell lines.

GRANULES OR
NO GRANULES

Cells of the immune system can also be classified according to whether or not they contain large granules. Granulocytes, sometimes referred to as polymorphonuclear leukocytes because of their lobed nuclei, make up most of your white blood cells and are involved in local inflammatory responses. They contain large granules that house substances capable of destroying microbes or that act as mediators coordinating local changes that support the destruction of these invaders. Neutrophils are the most abundant granulocytes: they are the infantry that first attack by engulfing and eating invaders.

Non-granulocytes contain few or no granules and typically have nuclei that are either large and spherical or kidney-shaped. They have their own big eater in the form of macrophages, which gobble up anything foreign or damaged. Some have the ability to regurgitate recognizable bits of their target, the antigens, onto their surface. These antigen-presenting cells (APC) pass this information onto lymphocytes. Dendritic cells are the main APCs and act as a messenger between the two divisions. They have nothing to do with the nervous system but have cytoplasmic processes that extend a bit like dendrites, hence the name. Lymphocytes are the predominant cells of the adaptive immune system and use the antigenic information provided to launch intelligence-based attacks.

▼ This scanning electron micrograph shows a neutrophil ingesting MRSA bacteria. Neutrophils are the first cells to appear when a pathogen invades.

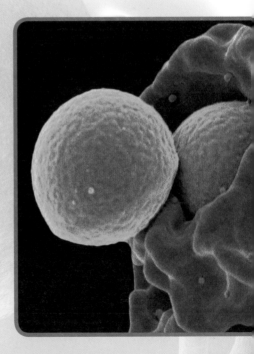

LEUKOCYTE AGENT PROFILES

	DIVISION/ SYSTEM	STEM CELL DYNASTY	GROWTH FACTOR (MAIN)	IMMATURE VERSION	MATURE VERSION	FEATURES	MODUS OPERANDI
Neutrophil	First/innate	Myeloid	Granulocyte colony stimulating factors (type of cytokine)	Myeloblast	Granulocyte (three types, all containing large granules in their cytoplasm)	Neutrophil: Segmented nucleus; granules hold digesting enzymes or chemicals	Phagocytic; first to arrive; targets bacteria and fungi; forms pus when it dies
Eosinophil						Eosinophil: Lobed nucleus; granules hold powerful enzymes or molecules	Targets parasites and bacteria; involved in allergic reactions; recruited from blood into tissues
Basophil						Basophil: Kidney-shaped nucleus; granules hold substances like histamine and heparin	Involved in allergic reactions; helps capillaries to dilate and signals other immune cells to the area
Mast cell			Stem cell factor (type of cytokine)	Progenitor mast cell (released into blood)	Mast cell (once resident in a tissue; a type of granulocyte)	Similar morphology to a basophil as it contains granules that release histamine (intensifies inflammation) and heparin (stops blood clotting)	Immature version migrates to connective tissues and becomes resident white blood cell; has similar properties to basophil; responsible for most allergic and inflammatory responses
Monocyte			Monocyte colony stimulating factors (type of cytokine)	Monoblast	Monocyte (non-granulocyte)	Kidney-shaped nucleus; the largest white blood cell	Phagocytosis; morphs into a macrophage in tissues to engulf and digest pathogens and cell debris

	DIVISION/ SYSTEM	STEM CELL DYNASTY	GROWTH FACTOR (MAIN)	IMMATURE VERSION	MATURE VERSION	FEATURES	MODUS OPERANDI
Natural killer cell	First/innate	Lymphoid	Interleukins (type of cytokine)	Lymphoblast	Natural killer cell (non-granulocyte)	Cytoplasm contains small granules with proteins that can kill cells	Targets tumour cells and cells with viruses; binds to cells that do not express 'self' proteins on membrane
Dendritic cell	In between innate and adaptive	Both	Depends on lineage	Immature dendritic cell (migrates from bone marrow to live in non-lymphoid tissues in contact with the external environment)	Mature dendritic cell (once they capture antigens and migrate to lymph node)	Has cytoplasmic processes that help sample its resident tissue for antigens	Phagocytosis; links both arms of the immune system; presents antigens to lymphocytes in lymph node
T-lymphocyte	Second/ adaptive	Lymphoid	Interleukins (type of cytokine)	Lymphoblast	T-lymphocyte (mature in thymus; non-granulocyte; two main types)	T-helper cell or cytotoxic T-cell	T-helper cell helps activate B- and cytotoxic T-cells and signals to coordinate attacks. Cytotoxic T-cell acts like a natural killer but binds to cells expressing proteins that show it is infected with a virus or is cancerous
B-lymphocyte					B-lymphocyte (non-granulocyte)	Large nucleus	Once activated, produces antibodies that mark foreign substances for destruction by macrophages; helps clump and quarantine pathogens

ACTIVATE THE LYMPHOCYTES!

There are two types of lymphocytes: B- and T-cells. These special recruits of the second division undergo specific training in the bone marrow or thymus to ensure they have the ability to recognize self from non-self before being released into the circulation and taking up residence in lymphoid tissues or organs.

B-LYMPHOCYTES

B-lymphocytes are involved in your humoural response. They help attack free-floating pathogens in your tissue fluid, or humour, which have not yet penetrated any cell. B-cells develop protein ammunitions called antibodies that bind to a particular pathogen.

Each B-cell has thousands of a particular antibody bound to their surface. These B-cell receptors bind to a pathogen at a specific part called the epitope. Like a tiger lying in wait in your lymph nodes, B-cells bind to an antigen passing through and ingest it via receptor-mediated endocytosis. This is similar to phagocytosis except it requires a specific antigen to bind to the B-cell receptor, whereas phagocytosis is non-specific. The B-cell then acts as an APC and presents part of the antigen on its membrane in a receptor complex called Major Histocompatibility Complex type II (MHC II).

Primed for its next transformation, the B-cell waits for a type of T-lymphocyte called a T-helper cell (which itself has been activated by the same antigen) to bind to its MHC II complex, which releases cytokines that fully activate the B-cell. This failsafe mechanism double checks that the B-cell has received the right

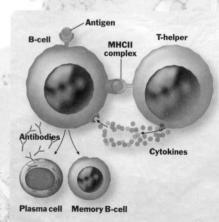

▲ B-cell activation is a multistep process.

information before it starts cloning itself. The B-cell differentiates into two types of cells: (1) a plasma cell which makes free-floating antibodies that enter the bloodstream and can bind to the foreign antigen at its epitope, and (2) a long-lived memory cell which remembers the antigen for future reference.

ANTIBODIES

An antibody is a globular protein, or immunoglobulin (Ig), produced by plasma cells. It has two arms and a tail called the Fc region. It is composed of four protein chains, two of which are heavy and two light. The two tips of the arms form the variable region, or domain, which differs from antibody to antibody and provides the antibody with its specificity. The part of the tip that binds to a specific antigen (in a lock and key scenario) is called the paratope. The rest of the antibody is conserved among different classes, or isotypes, and is called the constant domain. The five immunoglobulin isotypes are:

IgG: The most common antibody in serum and the only antibody capable of crossing the placenta.

▲ *An antibody is Y-shaped.*

IgE: The least common antibody in serum, it binds to basophils and mast cells.

IgM: The largest antibody, this is also the first type of antibody produced during an immune response.

IgA: The most common antibody in bodily secretions.

IgD: Involved in the maturation and activation of B-cells.

Antibodies stop pathogens in their tracks using the following methods:

Tag them (opsonization): Helps phagocytes recognize them more easily and gobble them up.

Clump them together (agglutination or aggregation): Herding effect.

Disable them (neutralization): Completely surround them, preventing the pathogen from entering and infecting cells.

T-LYMPHOCYTES

Despite the efforts of the B-lymphocytes, cells do get infected by pathogens. To deal with this before all hope is lost, your body engages its final piece of artillery, the T-lymphocyte. In truth, this may happen before B-cell activation or simultaneously, but this is the last that remains. Your T-cells start off as immature versions of themselves in the thymus. They mature once they acquire T-cell receptors that are capable of distinguishing self from non-self and can bind to specific foreign antigens. Then the mature T-cells migrate via the blood to lymphoid tissue.

There are two main types of T-lymphocytes: T-helper and cytotoxic T-cells. They are distinguishable by their surface protein markers called CD4+ (T-helper) and CD8+ (cytotoxic T-cells). CD4+ cells bind via their T-cell receptor to antigens mounted on the MHC II complex of professional

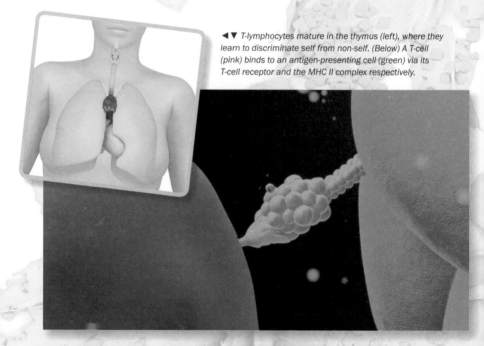

◄ ▼ *T-lymphocytes mature in the thymus (left), where they learn to discriminate self from non-self. (Below) A T-cell (pink) binds to an antigen-presenting cell (green) via its T-cell receptor and the MHC II complex respectively.*

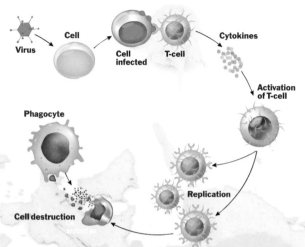

Virus → Cell → Cell infected → T-cell → Cytokines → Activation of T-cell

Phagocyte

Cell destruction

Replication

antigen-presenting cells (dendritic cells or macrophages). In contrast, CD8+ cells bind to any unhealthy cells that mount their antigens on an MHC I complex (any nucleated cell that is either infected with a pathogen or is abnormal, such as malignant cells). Either way, T-cells can only participate in battle once they are suitably activated upon binding.

Once stimulated, T-helper cells clone themselves. This is done to increase the available platoon of effector cells that can (1) recognize a specific foreign antigen and release cytokines that ramp up the immune response, and (2) activate cytotoxic T-cells that recognize the same antigen. As with the B-cells, they differentiate and also divide into long-lived memory cells that retain

▲ *Virally infected cells are recognized by T-cells, which mount a targeted immune response.*

the intelligence they have acquired for future secondary immune responses that will be faster.

Similarly, activated cytotoxic T-cells bound to an infected cell differentiate and clone themselves into memory and effector cells. The latter add insult to injury by spewing a deadly cocktail of cytokines and cytotoxic granules directly in the face of the tainted cell, which forms pores in its membrane allowing toxic substances to enter. Once inside, these substances wreak havoc and destroy all proteins inside the blighted cell, forcing it to commit suicide.

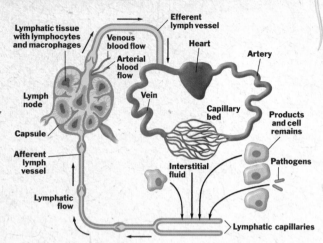

► Lymphatic capillaries are rooted in the capillary bed and drain the tissue fluid to form lymph, which travels in lymphatic vessels and through lymph nodes. Lymph carried by lymphatic ducts empties into the systemic circulation via the subclavian vein.

VESSELS AND ORGANS

Now let us look in more detail at the vessels and organs that transport and house these gallant cells of the immune system.

LYMPHATIC VESSELS

Lymphatic vessels run parallel to your arteries and veins and transport immune cells and various proteins, salts and fatty substances in a milky white concoction, similar to blood plasma, called lymph. Similarly to arteries, as they approach your tissues, the vessels divide into smaller branches and form porous lymphatic tubules, or capillaries, that root themselves in capillary beds. Capillary beds help to drain any leaked fluid bathing your tissues and prevent your cells from being soaked. Lymph is returned to your blood via two great vessels, or ducts, that each enter the bloodstream at the left or right subclavian veins. This ensures that the blood does not get too concentrated and gives the various immune cells access to the circulatory network so they can reach different parts of your body.

Unlike in your cardiovascular system, there is no lymphatic heart or pump. Instead, the lymph relies on the movement of your skeletal muscles to help propel it through their vasculature, which is another reason why exercising is a good thing. Valves within these vessels ensure the flow is one way.

LYMPH NODES

Dotted along the lymphatic vessels at various sites in your body are clusters of little bean-shaped structures called lymph nodes. Often erroneously referred to as 'glands', these beady chains of nodules provide a home for the lymphocytes involved in the adaptive immune system. T- and B-cells lie in wait here ready to pounce on any pathogens that made it into your bloodstream or any antigens presented to them. In doing so, the T- and B-cells effectively filter the lymph passing through as it makes its way back into the bloodstream.

Lymph nodes drain specific areas of your body: for example, those in the space between your collarbone and neck (supraclavicular nodes) mostly drain tissues and organs in your chest. Swollen lymph nodes are a sure-fire indication that you have an infection or a problem that has commandeered a response from the adaptive immune system. They become active and increase their immune cell colony to address the emergent issue.

BONE MARROW AND THYMUS

Primary lymphoid organs, namely your red bone marrow and thymus, are those structures that give birth to lymphocytes, and also nurture their ability to discriminate self from non-self. For the record, your thymus is not the same thing as your thyroid. The thyroid is a gland inside your neck that secretes hormones and looks a bit like a butterfly attached to your windpipe, while the thymus sits in your chest cavity just above your heart and allows T-lymphocytes to grow up.

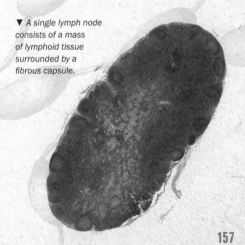

▼ A single lymph node consists of a mass of lymphoid tissue surrounded by a fibrous capsule.

SPLINTER RESPONSE

Let's take a closer look at the immune system by watching its response to a splinter piercing deeply. The splinter causes pain and tissue damage. The foreign body is still present and has brought bacteria with it.

FIRST LINE RESPONSE

The first response is inflammation:

- Damaged cells release cytokines.
- Granulocytes are attracted to the site by chemotaxis (chemical signals released by cells). Neutrophils are the first cells at the scene. They eat bacteria that entered the skin by engulfment and then release of granules. Afterward, the neutrophils die and accumulate to form pus.
- Local immune cells (macrophages and mast cells) are attracted to the wound. The mast cells release histamine, causing increased blood flow to the area, which makes it hot, red and inflamed.
- The macrophages engulf the bacteria by phagocytosis and clean up the debris left by the neutrophils.
- The nearest capillary swells and its walls become more porous to facilitate the passage of immune cells, platelets, plasma and complement proteins.
- Natural killer cells target any cells infected with viruses (if present).

▶ Mast cells are attracted to the wound. They release histamine, which causes capillaries to dilate and become leaky. Neutrophils move into the infected tissue. Increased blood flow causes the tissue to get hot and inflamed. Phagocytes engulf and digest bacteria, while dendritic cells present the antigen to lymphocytes for a potential adaptive immune response.

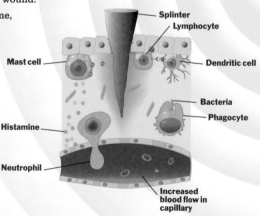

- Splinter
- Lymphocyte
- Mast cell
- Dendritic cell
- Bacteria
- Phagocyte
- Histamine
- Neutrophil
- Increased blood flow in capillary

COMPLEMENT SYSTEM

These are a set of over 30 proteins that circulate in the blood. In the event of tissue damage and the presence of pathogens, these proteins are activated and band together to kill free-floating pathogens, either directly or indirectly:

Direct attack: They form a structure called a Membrane Attack Complex, which digs a hole in the membrane surface of the target cell. This enables water, ions and small molecules to enter, eventually causing the cell to rupture.

Indirect attack: The proteins attract granulocytes, mast cells and phagocytic cells to the area, or they mark pathogens for phagocytosis.

PHAGOCYTOSIS

Macrophages, dendritic cells and neutrophils kill bacteria and antigens through phagocytosis:

1: The immune cell binds to the bacterium.

2: The phagocyte engulfs the pathogen like a boa constrictor, its membrane invaginating until it completely encircles the intruder.

3: The bacterium is contained in a vesicle within the macrophage known as a phagosome. A lysosome attaches and gives the bacterium a toxic shower by dumping its cytotoxic chemicals into the vesicles – and the bacterium is digested.

4: Those immune cells with antigen-presenting capabilities bind little bits of the digested bacterium or antigen to proteins called MHC II complexes. This is presented to cells of the second division (B- and T-lymphocytes) to determine what type of pathogen it is and decide whether to mount an appropriate response.

Pathogen

2

Phagocyte

1

T-helper cell

Particle of pathogen

MHC II

4

3

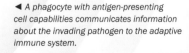

◀ *A phagocyte with antigen-presenting cell capabilities communicates information about the invading pathogen to the adaptive immune system.*

THE PLACE OF PLATELETS

Wound-healing begins with platelets, also known as thrombocytes. Although they are not immune cells, platelets defend you by forming clots to seal damaged skin and blood vessels. Platelets have an irregular surface, which acts like tiny limbs or pseudopods, allowing them to cling to vessel walls and each other.

Platelets are not cells, but cytoplasmic fragments of a blobby megakaryocyte. Megakaryocytes are derived from haematopoietic stem cells in the bone marrow, and are of the same lineage as mast cells, granulocytes and monocytes (including red blood cells). The myeloid progenitor cell that creates this lineage has to receive the liver-derived growth factor signal thrombopoietin before it differentiates into the megakaryoblast, a precursor of the megakaryocyte.

MAKING A SCAB

To seal a wound, activated platelets signal the blood vessels to contract as they stick to the wound. The platelets team up with a plasma protein called fibrinogen to form fibrin. This produces a jelly-like mesh of fibrous threads that trap blood cells and form a plug, which hardens into a scab as the serum dries.

Healing truly begins when the blood vessel re-opens and white blood cells rid the area of infective agents. Nearby fibroblast cells produce new collagen to aid more permanent repair. As the sides of the wound pull together, the clot dissolves by a process called fibrinolysis, in which enzymes break down the fibrin.

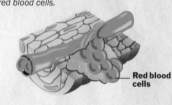

▶ *A damaged capillary leaks plasma and red blood cells.*

Red blood cells

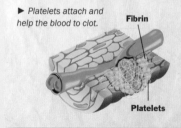

▶ *Platelets attach and help the blood to clot.*

Fibrin

Platelets

MAGGOTS

Sometimes wounds simply do not heal, especially those that are deep and have become necrotic. Such wounds bear cells that have died and accumulated en masse. The fact they died by necrosis meant phagocytes did not receive the signal to clear them up, so wound healing is delayed. It seems in these circumstances the dead and living cannot co-exist. Healing will only proceed once the area has been debrided, or cleared of dead tissue. Unless this happens, infection could set in and spread.

Cue the maggots, which are live (disinfected) fly larvae, applied directly into the wound. These larvae eat dead tissue and leave the live tissue. In addition, the antimicrobial substances the larvae release, designed to ensure that they feast uninterrupted by protecting them from bacteria, also have the effect of slowing down inflammation. Before any maggot treatment commences, it is vital to establish that the wound is of a type that would respond to this particular brand of biotherapy, as not all are suitable.

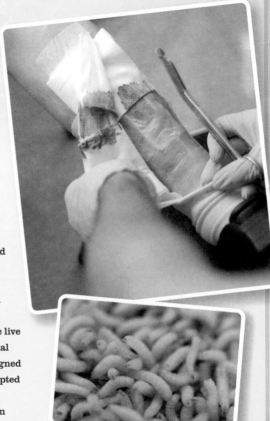

▲ Maggot therapy is an alternative way to treat certain wounds that refuse to heal. It removes dead tissue from the wound and also disinfects it.

HYPERSENSITIVITY REACTIONS

Not all foreign substances are harmful to your body. Sometimes your immune system malfunctions, overreacting to the slightest thing. Hypersensitivity reactions arise when your immune cells mount a disproportionate response to antigenic material. This results in an unnecessary amount of inflammation, which being non-specific causes collateral damage to your cells and tissues. There are four types of hypersensitivity reaction to contend with.

TYPE I HYPERSENSITIVITY

Type I describes the classic allergic response to allergens such as pollen, dust, pollution, insect bites and certain foods. It is usually immediate. Immunogenic responses involve the production of IgE antibodies that stimulate mast cells and basophils to release histamine. This chemical is at the centre of many associated symptoms, which although incapacitating can usually be managed with anti-histamine medication. However, anaphylaxis is a severe reaction in which histamine release goes ballistic and sends your body into shock. It can be deadly as it affects heartbeat, constricts airways and causes blood vessels to dilate excessively, resulting in a drop in blood pressure from which you can lose consciousness. An immediate shot of adrenaline is one of several first-aid responses.

▲ *Allergens secreted from cats' skin or in their saliva can trigger a Type I hypersensitivity response.*

TYPES II–IV HYPERSENSITIVITY

The other three hypersensitivity reactions can involve an autoimmune response. Autoimmunity arises when your adaptive immune cells fail the 'Discriminating Between Self and Non-Self' class and damage the things they are programmed to protect. There are more than 80 autoimmune diseases, including coeliac disease and multiple sclerosis (MS).

In Type II Hypersensitivity, B-cells produce antibodies that inappropriately mark cells for destruction by phagocytes or are rogue autoantibodies that attack 'self' cell membrane receptors or extracellular material.

Type III Hypersensitivity reactions cause collateral damage to your tissues due to antibody-antigen complexes lodging themselves in places such as your joints, kidneys or blood vessels, causing inflammation and damage.

Type IV Hypersensitivity does not involve any antibodies but rather is cell-mediated through activated T-cells. It arises when a non-threatening foreign antigen modifies your cells' proteins, which T-cells recognize as abnormal and elicit a targeted immune response which usually arises 24 to 72 hours from the initial exposure to the antigen.

IMMUNODEFICIENCY

In contrast to hypersensitivity, your immune system can fail to work at all. Being immunodeficient makes you vulnerable not just to life-threatening opportunistic infections but also to cancers, which your immune cells would usually constantly check for, by eliminating any mutated cell.

Immunodeficiency can arise because of a genetic defect or from a secondary event. For example, following infection with human immunodeficiency virus (HIV), a poor diet, or medical treatments such as chemotherapy (which damage the bone marrow) or organ transplants

(when the recipients take strong immuno-suppressant drugs). When the cause of immunodeficiency is medical treatment, there is often a balancing act weighing the risks from using the drugs against the therapeutic benefits they bring.

▼ *The HIV virus infects T-helper cells, dendritic cells and macrophages.*

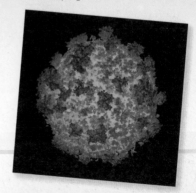

REBOUNDING: FAD OR PANACEA?

Rebounding is a form of exercise that involves jumping up and down on a mini trampoline. It is certainly a fun way to keep fit, but proponents of the exercise claim that it offers many 'scientifically proven' health benefits that leave traditional forms of exercise way behind.

In 1980, scientists from the US National Aeronautics and Space Agency (NASA) published the findings of research they conducted on eight men aged 19 to 26 years for the purposes of understanding more about deconditioning in astronauts exposed to weightlessness and microgravity. They compared jumping on a trampoline with other forms of impact exercise in the same individuals a week apart and measured the amount of oxygen consumed, heart rate and the G-force experienced at various joints along the length of the body using sensitive accelerometer devices. What they reported alluded to the fact that rebounding was gentler on the joints due to its association with comparatively lower G-forces, while also being significantly more efficient at using oxygen and working out your muscles.

A whole health and fitness industry has since formed on the back of this and a few other studies published at the time. Enthusiasts purport rebounding helps improve cardiovascular and eye health, proprioception and bone density; aids diabetes prevention and control; provides cells with an internal massage; and promotes healing. One significant claim is rebounding's superior ability to stimulate your lymphatic system. Indeed, it has been said to provide the lymphatic circulatory benefits of jogging without the associated impact on your joints.

Whether rebounding is a panacea for many of today's common ailments and diseases remains to be seen as more research is needed to build on the anecdotal evidence that suggests it is. Unfortunately, there exist very few peer-reviewed scientific studies or clinical trials to confirm or refute the above claims; although, in recent years, it appears the tide may be turning. Certainly, rebounding warrants wider scientific exploration to determine its true value in maintaining health and preventing disease.

THE HEALTH BOUNCE

Rebounding is considered to be such an easy exercise that it can be performed with relatively no skill, even by those deemed unfit (although, to be safe, get the green light from your physician and use a support frame). It is certainly a fun and gentle form of cardio exercise. The 'health bounce' involves gently bouncing without your feet leaving the mat and is best performed from heel-to-toe for maximal effect. This subtle movement performed for several minutes apparently helps to open and close the valves in your lymphatic vessels, thereby assisting the flow of lymph through your system – the changes in gravitational force as you bounce helping to pulse the lymph. This in turn is believed to improve your immune function by preventing lymph from stagnating and tissues from being bogged down with waste products.

▶ Rebounding is believed to optimize the flow of lymph through your body.

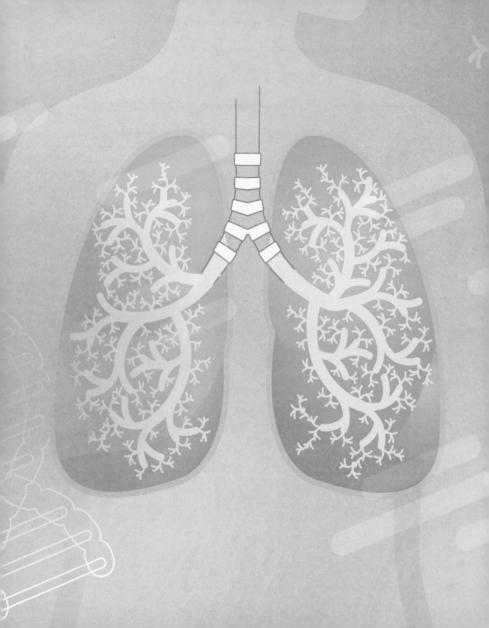

CHAPTER 7

A PARAMOUNT EXCHANGE

THE RESPIRATORY SYSTEM

With each breath you take, something quite amazing happens inside your chest. A very special exchange occurs between your blood and the air. Breathing provides the component needed to convert the food you eat into energy and a way out for the by-products that arise from using this life-giving gas.

The organs, structures and tissues that help you draw in oxygen and expel carbon dioxide and water make up your respiratory system. This includes more than just your lungs, as your breathing apparatus reels in your mouth, nose, pharynx, larynx, trachea, bronchi, bronchioles and alveoli to share the responsibility for getting O_2 in and CO_2 out. However, your respiratory system does more than just help you exchange these gases, as it also exploits the airflow to help you communicate through sounds and to discriminate different scents that hitch a ride in the air.

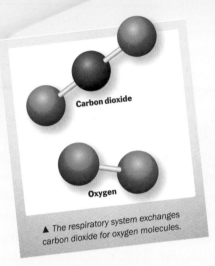

▲ The respiratory system exchanges carbon dioxide for oxygen molecules.

CONDUCTION AND RESPIRATION

The respiratory tract can be divided anatomically into the upper and lower regions: the dividing point is in your neck where the pharynx meets the larynx. From a functional perspective, there are two zones: the conduction and respiratory zones. Each collates structures according to whether they provide the infrastructure for the air to flow (conduction) or the platform for exchange of gases (respiration).

The mechanics of breathing is known as ventilation and encompasses two equal and opposite events: inspiration (inhalation) and expiration (exhalation). Both rely on the contraction and relaxation of muscles in your ribcage (intercostal muscles), diaphragm and abdominal regions. This is all controlled, without your awareness, in specific respiratory centres of your brain and receptors in your arteries that detect high levels of carbon dioxide or low levels of oxygen in your blood and signal your muscles to act accordingly.

The actual exchange itself is driven by differences in pressure across the lung border that compel the gases to diffuse from high to low concentrations.

The transport of these gases in the blood differs. Oxygen is mostly contained in haemoglobin in red blood cells while carbon dioxide mostly travels in plasma as the compound bicarbonate.

RESPIRATORY SYSTEM

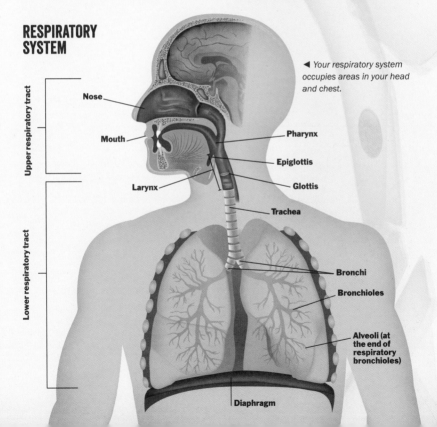

◄ *Your respiratory system occupies areas in your head and chest.*

Upper respiratory tract

- Nose
- Mouth
- Larynx

- Pharynx
- Epiglottis
- Glottis
- Trachea

Lower respiratory tract

- Bronchi
- Bronchioles
- Alveoli (at the end of respiratory bronchioles)
- Diaphragm

THE CONDUCTION ZONE

'You are travelling through another dimension, a dimension not only of heat and mucus but of beating ciliated cells. A journey into a wondrous expanse whose boundaries are overcome by the act of diffusion. Your next stop, the Conduction Zone!' That is what you might say to an oxygen molecule as it entered your nose or mouth – if you were a fan of *The Twilight Zone*... In the conduction zone, oxygen meets a fantastic assortment of substances, cells and structures that aim to make its passage to the other side as streamlined as possible.

▼ *A scanning electron micrograph shows cilia of nasal epithelial cells trapping bacteria (yellow) in the nose.*

NASAL CAVITY

First comes your nasal cavity, which is divided into ridges of bone called concha, or turbinates, that form passages known as a meatuses. These grooves expand the surface area of your nasal cavity, forcing the inhaled air down passageways that allow it to brush the majority of nasal cells. This is important because these epithelial cells, which bear microscopic hairlike projections called cilia, help warm the incoming air by virtue of their rich blood supply. They also remove debris and pathogens trapped in the mucus made by the nasal mucous membrane.

RESPIRATORY TREE

The lower part of the respiratory system is not called a respiratory tree or tracheobronchial tree for nothing: it actually looks like one too. Indeed, you will find that branching and tree-like formations are a common pattern in nature, from snowflakes and river networks to lightning. This fractal arrangement arises in your airways because it provides maximal surface area for gas absorption within a very confined space.

▲ *Branching also appears on a macro scale, as illustrated by this aerial photograph showing river tributaries.*

TRACHEA

As the inhaled air passes the pharynx and larynx regions of your throat, it enters the largest tube in the respiratory tract: your windpipe, or trachea. This cartilaginous structure, which sits in front of your oesophagus, is supported by up to 20 C-shaped tracheal rings. It forms the beginning of your lower respiratory tract.

BRONCHI TO BRONCHIOLES

As air is drawn further down, it comes to a fork where the trachea splits into two passageways called bronchi. The first of many divisions, this unfolding symmetry repeats itself about 23 times. Bronchi and subsequent branches called bronchioles contain beating hair-like cilia that help move mucus (made by goblet cells and submucosal glands) up toward the throat before being swallowed. Bronchioles represent the end of the conduction zone and the entrance to the next stop – the respiratory zone. All change!

THE RESPIRATORY ZONE

As the air travels further down, it reaches the terminal ends of the bronchioles, the most distal segment of the conduction zone. Air is now in respiratory zone territory. From this point onward, an oxygen molecule will increasingly find structures that are directly involved in gaseous exchange.

▲ *Ciliated epithelia are present in the respiratory zone all the way down through to respiratory bronchioles.*

TERMINAL BRONCHIOLES

The epithelial lining begins to change, becoming thinner. It also swaps mucus-secreting cells for those capable of producing a detergent-like substance called surfactant. This secretion helps to reduce any surface tension that arises to ensure the bronchioles expand during inspiration and do not collapse during expiration.

RESPIRATORY BRONCHIOLES

Travelling deeper still, the terminal bronchioles narrow down to 0.5mm ($^{1}/_{50}$in) and form the respiratory bronchioles, representing the final bronchiole division in the respiratory zone. They are held together by smooth muscle and elastic fibres. Their walls sprout alveolar ducts that connect them to spongy tissue resembling mounds of microscopic profiteroles called alveolar sacs, only each individual profiterole, or alveolus, is filled with nothing but air and drizzled

AIRWAY SMOOTH MUSCLE

The walls of the airways contain smooth muscle and elastin that expand or contract. This feature is thought to help regulate air flow into the lungs. During exercise, greater volumes of air are required, so smooth muscle responds by relaxing to dilate the airways. Bronchodilation and bronchoconstriction are coordinated by the autonomic nervous system. The smooth muscles become inflamed and thickened in asthma, causing narrowing of the airways and symptoms of bronchoconstriction: coughing, wheezing and shortness of breath.

with capillaries instead of chocolate. Exchange happens in this most distal part of the airways.

When the cells that line a pulmonary capillary meet the inner lining of an alveolus, they form something quite unique, an air-blood barrier called the respiratory membrane that provides the platform for oxygen and carbon dioxide to cross by diffusion. Together with the bronchial tree and pulmonary vasculature (see page 127) these structures collectively form your lungs.

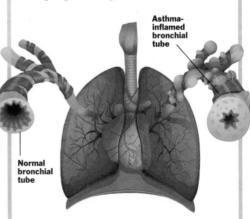

Asthma-inflamed bronchial tube

Normal bronchial tube

▲ Asthma typically arises following exposure to allergens, pollutants, exercise or cold air. These cause inflammation, leading to airway constriction.

LOVELY LUNGS

Your lungs would send any de-cluttering guru into a panic, as they are exceptionally skilled at packing lots into small spaces. Your chest contains about 2,400km (1,500 miles) of airways and over 500 million alveoli. Furthermore, to optimize the extraction of oxygen from the air, your lungs have a surface area ranging from 50 to 70sq m (540 to 750sq ft).

One lung is to the left of your heart, the other to the right. Both are protected in the chest cavity, or thorax, by your rib cage. The lung on your right is much larger, because it has three lobes instead of two. The left lung is slightly smaller because it has to accommodate a bit of

your heart and so creates a cubbyhole called the cardiac notch. The functional unit of the lungs is the pulmonary lobule (see page 176). It comprises a single respiratory bronchiole that branches off into alveolar ducts that form alveolar sacs containing individual alveoli.

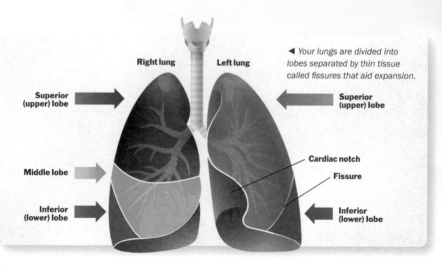

Right lung   Left lung

◄ Your lungs are divided into lobes separated by thin tissue called fissures that aid expansion.

Superior (upper) lobe

Superior (upper) lobe

Middle lobe

Cardiac notch

Fissure

Inferior (lower) lobe

Inferior (lower) lobe

A SPECIAL RELATIONSHIP

Your lungs have a special relationship with your heart. Instead of your heart just sending the lungs oxygenated blood like it does with all other tissues, the heart also sends them deoxygenated blood via the pulmonary circulation (see page 127). This means your lungs effectively have two circulations, one for nourishment and another solely to do their job. The oxygenated blood the lungs receive is provided by the bronchial circulation from bronchial arteries that branch off the aorta.

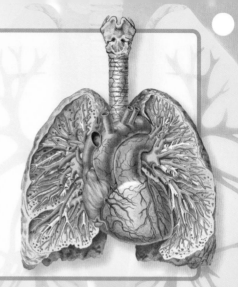

PULMONARY PLEURAE

Each lung is encased within a pleural sac, a double tissue membrane that folds back on itself to form two pulmonary pleurae. The first, known as the visceral pleura, lines the surface of the lungs, including the fissures that make up the lobes. The second, known as the parietal pleura, is continuous with the inner lining of the thorax.

PULMONARY FLUID

The space in between the pleurae, called the pleural cavity, is filled with pleural fluid produced by the mesothelial cells that make up these tissue membranes. This lubrication is very much needed.

Not only does it reduce friction by allowing the inner and outer walls to slide over each other as your lungs expand and contract during breathing, but the surface tension produced in the cavity sticks the lungs to the thoracic wall. Without this tension, the lungs would deflate and collapse like a balloon. This happens during a pneumothorax, or collapsed lung, where a tear in the lung allows air to leak into the pleural cavity. It can be caused by trauma or an underlying lung condition. Depending on severity, a pneumothorax can either heal on its own or require aspiration of excess air via a needle or chest tube inserted into the ribs.

THE EXCHANGE PLATFORM

Alveoli provide the surface area for gaseous exchange. To understand how oxygen and carbon dioxide cross the respiratory surface, it helps to understand the principles of two basic gas laws envisioned by the English chemists John Dalton (1766–1844) and William Henry (1774–1836). However, as this is not a chemistry and physics text book, what you really need to know is that gases exert pressure. Think of blowing up a balloon until it bursts – that's pressure for you!

There are three types of cells in the alveoli. The first two are called pneumocytes. Type I forms the flattened walls of the alveoli sacs upon which gas diffusion occurs. Type II are more cuboidal in shape and secrete a mixture of proteins and fatty compounds called the pulmonary surfactant into the alveolar space. This helps to reduce the surface tension created by the water expired so that the alveoli and ultimately the lung can expand without any pressure.

The third group of cells are alveolar macrophages, which protect the airspaces from pathogens that have made it this far. Failure could lead to serious infections such as pneumonia, which arises when the air sacs inflame and fill with fluid or pus. Aspiration pneumonia arises when you inhale substances other than air into your lung, such as vomit, stomach acid, food or drink. Symptomatic relief or treatment with antibiotics or antiviral medication is usually effective in most cases.

▶ External respiration takes place in an alveolus (right), which forms part of a pulmonary lobule (left).

Alveoli

Carbon dioxide
Oxygen
Alveolar wall
Air
Capillary
Carbon dioxide out
Red blood cell
Oxygen in

MOVING FROM HIGH TO LOW PRESSURE

Each gas molecule exerts its own amount of pressure, or partial pressure, which is related to its concentration. Like liquids, gases move from areas of high pressure to low pressure. Therefore, at the respiratory surface, carbon dioxide moves from a region of high partial pressure (in the pulmonary capillary) to a region of low partial pressure (the alveolar airspace). Oxygen moves in the opposite direction, from a region of its high partial pressure (the alveolar airspace) to its region of low partial pressure (pulmonary capillary). This occurs until an equilibrium is reached.

If for any reason there are insufficient levels of oxygen in the airspace of an alveolus, making the partial pressure low there, the capillaries cleverly constrict to prevent loss of oxygen and redirect the blood to another alveolus where the partial pressure in its airspace is sufficiently higher. As the deoxygenated red blood cells pass through the respiratory surface, the carbon dioxide diffuses out and the oxygen diffuses in and reoxygenates the blood.

RESPIRATION

Remember that, when we are using the term 'respiration' here, we are referring to gaseous exchange, not the production of energy that occurs with cellular respiration (glucose + oxygen → carbon dioxide + water + energy).

External respiration occurs only at the alveoli. Partial pressures are such that:

   O_2 in the alveolar airspace diffuses → blood

   CO_2 in the blood diffuses → the alveolar airspace

Internal respiration occurs at all tissues. Partial pressures are such that:

   O_2 in the blood diffuses → extracellular fluid → cells

   CO_2 in the cells diffuses → extracellular fluid → blood

IN AND OUT

The average person does it over 17,000 times a day, sometimes an additional 6,000 times. Despite this, you may be surprised to learn that many people do not even know how to breathe properly. Most of us use only a small proportion of our lung capacity to breathe, which is thought to contribute to many health complaints, including high blood pressure, stress and anxiety.

▲ If you are finding exercise increasingly difficult and get out of breath quite easily, you could have a problem with your diaphragm (or the nerves that supply it).

The act of breathing, known as pulmonary ventilation, is split into inspiration and expiration. As you breathe in, that muscular fibrous dome that separates your chest from your abdomen, called your diaphragm, contracts downward. Simultaneously, your intercostal muscles, which run between your ribs, contract upward. This causes your ribcage to expand and project outward, which increases your lung volume, causing the pressure to fall below that in the atmosphere and forcing air to be drawn into your lungs. Upon expiration, the muscles relax and your lungs and thorax recoil back, causing the air pressure to increase in your lungs and the air to be expelled out.

DIAPHRAGM

The diaphragm has a white, fibrous central portion with holes for your large blood vessels and oesophagus, and voluntary muscle at its periphery attached to surrounding structures. It receives instructions to contract or relax by phrenic nerves (left and right) that originate in your neck. Damage to these nerves can lead to paralysis of the diaphragm, depending on whether both sides are affected. Unilateral paralysis is often asymptomatic and detected upon incidental X-rays. Bilateral paralysis manifests itself as poor exercise tolerance, shortness of breath and fatigue.

BREATHING RATE

How often you breathe is usually a sign of how fit you are. The rate is dependent on the carbon dioxide levels in your blood rather than on how much oxygen it contains. Your brain, or more specifically regions called the medulla oblongata and pons in the brainstem, contain chemoreceptors that can detect pH changes in the blood. Acidity is linked to higher levels of hydrogen ions caused by the presence of carbon dioxide. The medulla oblongata regulates involuntary ventilation by sending signals to the muscles involved, while the pons controls the rate of breathing. Damage to these structures is often fatal.

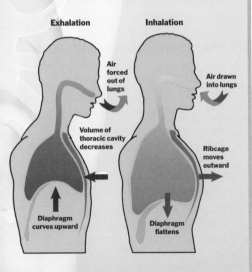

Exhalation	Inhalation
Air forced out of lungs	Air drawn into lungs
Volume of thoracic cavity decreases	Ribcage moves outward
Diaphragm curves upward	Diaphragm flattens

▲ *Breathing involves the interplay of various structures that work together to keep you alive.*

BLOOD TRANSPORT

The air you breathe contains only about 21 per cent oxygen, with the rest made up of nitrogen, argon, carbon dioxide, hydrogen and neon. Yet your respiratory system only extracts oxygen from the air: it owes this ability to haemoglobin's affinity for oxygen.

CARRYING OXYGEN

Though relatively little oxygen is transported in plasma itself, it must first dissolve in plasma before it can enter a red blood cell (see pages 132–5). Most oxygen travels around in the form of oxyhaemoglobin in red blood cells. Oxygen loading refers to the binding of oxygen to haemoglobin, which occurs in the lungs, while oxygen unloading occurs in metabolizing tissues and describes how oxygen dissociates from haemoglobin (resulting in deoxyhaemoglobin) and diffuses into the plasma en route to cells. Various factors favour unloading, such as increased temperature, carbon dioxide concentration and acidity.

CARRYING CARBON DIOXIDE

Carbon dioxide is transported in your blood in three different ways. Most of it gets around in the form of bicarbonate: when the carbon dioxide that diffuses from tissues enters a red blood cell, it gets converted into a bicarbonate by an enzyme called carbonic anhydrase before diffusing into the plasma in this form. This helps to control the acidity of blood. Once bicarbonate reaches the lungs, it jumps back into a red blood cell and undergoes reconversion before diffusing out as a free carbon dioxide molecule.

A lesser amount of carbon dioxide binds directly to haemoglobin and forms carbaminohaemoglobin. Whether this happens depends on how saturated the haemoglobin is with oxygen. A very small amount of carbon dioxide is dissolved in plasma itself.

◄ *This is a model of the molecular structure of oxyhaemoglobin, the principal mode of oxygen transport in your blood.*

PRINTING 3D LUNGS

'One lung ventilation' or 'lung isolation' is a term used in thoracic anaesthesia to describe the selective ventilation of one of a patient's lungs during surgery, which results in the other lung collapsing. This procedure is often carried out in order to perform surgery on the collapsed lung or nearby structures. It is usually performed using an endobronchial tube, inserted into the trachea and down into one of the two bronchi. However, anaesthesiologists with limited experience can find it difficult to obtain lung isolation in theatre, especially if the patient has a challenging airway. Current methods to develop skills in lung isolation include mannequins and virtual reality simulators. However, a group of US physicians in Cleveland, Ohio, led by Dr Sergio Bustamante, conducted a study on the use of 3D printing technology. Using CT scans of a 'normal' airway and one that posed difficulties during a lung isolation in theatre, they recreated 3D models of each airway, which were then used for teaching.

▼ *3D printing technology could be used as part of preoperative evaluation for patients with unique airway anatomy.*

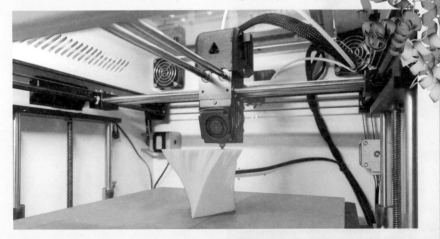

RESPIRATORY ANTICS

Respiratory reflexes help protect the airways from potentially harmful inhaled irritants. They also regulate your breathing under specific circumstances. Airway-linked events, such as crying and laughing, are triggered by emotional centres in the brain. However, it remains unclear why or how you hiccup and yawn.

	CONTROL	CAUSES	AIM	STAGES
Sneezing	Involuntary	Irritant particles entering the nose	To remove the irritant and clear your upper airways	(1) Nerve endings are irritated. (2) Air is forced down the throat. (3) The eyes and glottis (vocal cords) close. (4) Respiratory and abdominal muscles contract, forcing the glottis open. (5) Air is forced out through the nose and mouth.
Snoring	Involuntary	Partial collapse of the airways: the tongue falls back and the throat muscles collapse	None: snoring is an affliction	(1) Inhalation. (2) The soft palate at the back of the throat vibrates as air flows. (3) The vibration passes down to the throat and produces characteristic sounds.
Coughing	Involuntary	Irritant particles entering the lungs or excessive mucus in the lungs	To remove the irritant	(1) Cough receptors in the trachea and bronchi are irritated. (2) A brief inhalation as respiratory muscles contract to expand the lungs. (3) Pressure rises in the lungs as the diaphragm relaxes and the glottis snaps shut. (4) The intercostal muscles contract, forcing an explosion of air out.

	CONTROL	CAUSES	AIM	STAGES
Hiccups	Involuntary	Nerves in the diaphragm are stimulated	Unknown	(1) The diaphragm contracts, involuntarily forcing a rush of air into the lungs. (2) The glottis is forced shut and forms the hic sound.
Yawning	Involuntary	Unknown	An evolutionary response to signal tiredness	(1) Blood levels of carbon dioxide increase. (2) Inhalation is triggered to draw more oxygen into the body. (3) The face and jaw muscles stretch.
Laughing	Involuntary/ voluntary	Emotional stimuli	A social tool: to bond with others	(1) The emotional centres of the brain are activated. (2) The brain triggers contraction of the facial muscles. (3) A flap of cartilage in the throat, called the epiglottis, partly closes the larynx, causing irregular intakes of air that produce characteristic sound. (4) Strong gasps can follow and, sometimes, tear glands are activated.
Crying	Involuntary/ voluntary	Emotional stimuli	A social tool: to elicit support from others or to strengthen bonds	(1) The emotional centres of the brain are activated. (2) The tear glands and mucus glands in the nose are activated. (3) The glottis expands to increase air flow and also simultaneously tries to close, producing the 'lump in the throat'. (4) Air is forced through the glottis as the diaphragm relaxes and respiratory muscles contract.

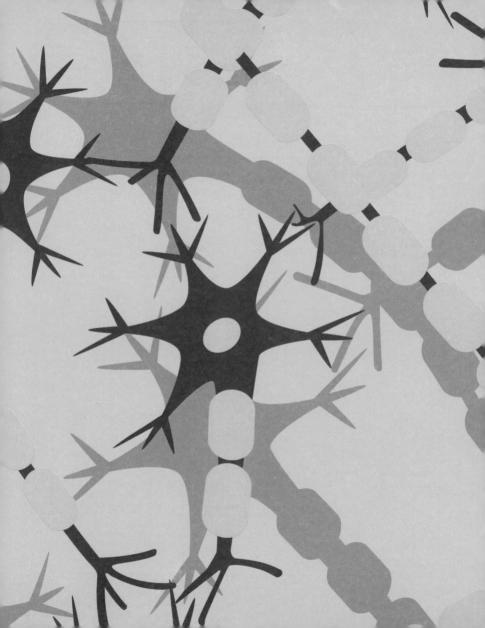

CHAPTER 8

THE HUB

THE NERVOUS SYSTEM

If your organ systems had a leader, it would be your nervous system. It provides the means by which many physiological systems check in before they act. It controls everything you do, regulates your basic functions and helps you move. It allows you to make sense of the world, think, remember and learn, while honing your discrimination between what is pleasurable and what could bring you pain.

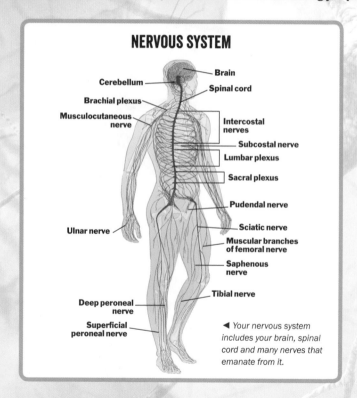

NERVOUS SYSTEM

- Brain
- Cerebellum
- Spinal cord
- Brachial plexus
- Musculocutaneous nerve
- Intercostal nerves
- Subcostal nerve
- Lumbar plexus
- Sacral plexus
- Pudendal nerve
- Ulnar nerve
- Sciatic nerve
- Muscular branches of femoral nerve
- Saphenous nerve
- Tibial nerve
- Deep peroneal nerve
- Superficial peroneal nerve

◄ Your nervous system includes your brain, spinal cord and many nerves that emanate from it.

The human nervous system is the most highly developed in the animal kingdom. As such, it is encased in the finest bone armoury and is cushioned in its own tailor-made interstitial and cerebrospinal fluid.

This most complex of organ systems has two main divisions: your central nervous system (CNS), which includes your brain and spinal cord, and your peripheral nervous system (PNS), which describes the nerves that emanate and spread out from the CNS into the rest of your body. The latter is further subdivided according to whether it innervates structures that you control voluntarily, in the somatic division, or those default functions that are centrally controlled without your conscious input, in the autonomic division. The autonomic nervous system tends to control things you cannot live without.

At the cellular level, the neuron, or nerve cell fibre, is the darling of the entire network. It lights up your whole system and excites everything it touches, generating electricity wherever it goes. It switches your brain on to what is going on and stimulates action.

VERY PERSONAL COMPUTER

Imagine your nervous system as a computer with no 'off' button. Your CNS would be the motherboard, executing and controlling what you do. It allows communication between different connectors or peripherals and provides a live adaptive integrated circuit. It takes messages it receives from your body's sensory equipment and analyses them before issuing a command. It includes a hard drive where information is stored in the memory system. Your PNS would be the computer's wires and cables. Its nerves either provide input to the motherboard or effect the commands and deliver output actions.

NEUROGLIA

Neuroglia, also called glia or glial cells, form the connective tissue of your nervous system. Although incapable of sending impulses, these cells are very capable at supporting and protecting those cells that do. Neuroglia far outnumber neurons and make up half the weight of your brain. They most often give rise to brain tumours, for neurons are incapable of division and therefore rarely form them. Neuroglia come in three different varieties: macroglia, microglia and ependymal cells.

MACROGLIA

In the CNS, there are two main types of macroglia: astrocytes and oligodendrocytes. Astrocytes look like stars and put their foot-like processes down on capillaries to help form the blood–brain barrier. They also do other amazing things that add to their star-like qualities, like repair damaged neurons and feed hungry neurons either by converting glucose into something more palatable or anchoring neurons to receive nutrients from the blood. They prop neurons up in the matrix they secrete, and ensure the extracellular environment is perfect in terms of ion content to support neuronal communication.

Oligodendrocytes help neurons in the CNS speed up their communication by wrapping a white fatty substance called myelin around the axon of the neuron. This forms an electrically insulating sheath that increases the speed at which the electrochemical impulse is transmitted. Myelin is actually an extension of the oligodendrocyte cell membrane that tightly winds itself around the fibres. One oligodendrocyte

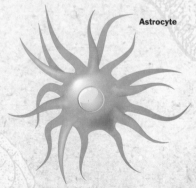

Astrocyte

Oligodendrocyte

MICROGLIA

These small, shapeshifting cells are the resident macrophages of your CNS. They consume pathogens, as well as neurons that have been damaged following a stroke or injury. They are the housekeepers of the CNS and restore balance when things go awry. In the PNS, this role is performed when satellite cells release substances that attract macrophages to the site.

can extend its processes to 50 different axons. Indeed, it is because of myelination that your brain and spinal cord have white matter.

Macroglia in the PNS include satellite cells, which perform a similar role to astrocytes in the CNS, by helping to regulate the extracellular environment. Myelination in the PNS is performed by Schwann cells, which wrap their entire cell body around axons. A 1m (3ft 4in) long nerve fibre can be wrapped in several thousand Schwann cells.

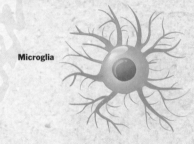

Microglia

Schwann cell

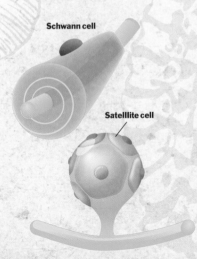

Satelllite cell

EPENDYMAL CELLS

These cells line your spinal cord and the ventricles of your brain. They form the choroid plexus that produces the cerebrospinal fluid (CSF). Their hair-like cilia help waft the CSF around the CNS.

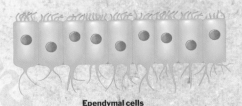

Ependymal cells

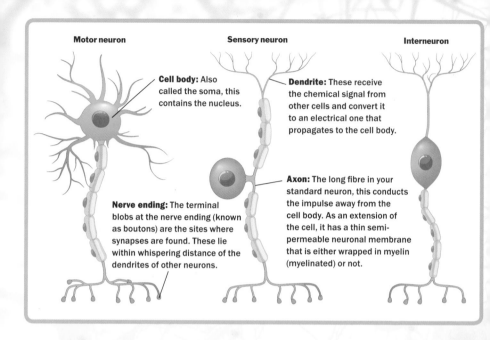

Motor neuron

Cell body: Also called the soma, this contains the nucleus.

Sensory neuron

Dendrite: These receive the chemical signal from other cells and convert it to an electrical one that propagates to the cell body.

Interneuron

Axon: The long fibre in your standard neuron, this conducts the impulse away from the cell body. As an extension of the cell, it has a thin semi-permeable neuronal membrane that is either wrapped in myelin (myelinated) or not.

Nerve ending: The terminal blobs at the nerve ending (known as boutons) are the sites where synapses are found. These lie within whispering distance of the dendrites of other neurons.

NEURONS

You have about 100 billion neurons, which pick up signals and send them either to another neuron or to a muscle or gland. Neurons come in many shapes and sizes, from a millionth of a centimetre in the case of interneurons, to 1m (3ft 4in) long in the case of a sensory neuron that travels from your toe to the end of your spinal cord.

TYPES OF NEURONS

Sensory, or afferent, neurons convey information from receptors in your sense organs to your CNS. Interneurons act as go-betweens, sending messages to neighbouring cells to analyse and process information or simply to relay to different neurons within a nerve circuit. Motor, or efferent, neurons carry signals away from the CNS to tissues to effect voluntary or involuntary commands.

PASSING ON SIGNALS

It all starts when the neuron gets excited at its dendrites. An electrical signal or action potential (AP) is generated and sent direct to the cell body before it enters the axon. The electrochemical signal then pulses along the length of the axon fibre. If the axon has a myelin jacket on, the AP travels even faster by salutatory conduction as it jumps between every unmyelinated gap or 'node of Ranvier', sometimes reaching speeds of up to 120m (390ft) per second. These nodes ensure that the AP does not dissipate once it reaches the nerve ending, where the signal is converted into a chemical one at the synapse. Different forms of chemical neurotransmitters transfer the message across the synaptic gap between two neurons.

A neuron can repeat this process up to 1,000 times each second. Multiply that by the potential number of synaptic connections one single neuron can make with other neurons (between 2,000 and 11,000) and you can see why neurons are the most energy-hungry components of your brain. As a child's brain constantly grows and forms new synaptic connections, the brain demands at least 40 per cent of their calorie intake. Microglial cells snip away any unused synapses in a process known as synaptic pruning to help reduce maintenance and conserve resources.

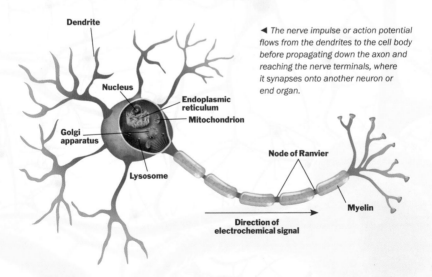

◄ The nerve impulse or action potential flows from the dendrites to the cell body before propagating down the axon and reaching the nerve terminals, where it synapses onto another neuron or end organ.

191

SECURING THE BRAIN

Your brain is your most protected organ. To get right into your head, one has to contend with several barriers, the first the skin and then the skull. A further layer is the meninges.

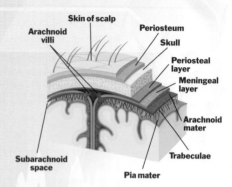

▲ The meninges includes the dura mater (periosteal and meningeal layers), arachnoid mater and pia mater.

THE MENINGES

The meninges provides a trinity of protective fibrous membranes called the dura mater, arachnoid mater and pia mater. The subarachnoid space separates the arachnoid mater from the pia mater. The meninges also covers your spinal cord, because like the brain it developed from the same neural tube that emerged from the ectodermal layer of an embryo.

CEREBROSPINAL FLUID

Cerebrospinal fluid (CSF) is a special form of tissue fluid, which is normally clear and watery. You produce about 500ml (1pt) of it daily. Some is secreted by cells in the pia mater but most is supplied by a network of capillaries and specialized ependymal cells at sites called choroid plexus that line ventricles. Ventricles are cavities in your brain. The subarachnoid space is filled with CSF.

In addition to protecting your brain from injury, CSF supplies the cortex and deeper structures with nutrients. Your CNS is physically isolated from your blood, via the blood–brain barrier, because neurons require a constant level of glucose, which fluctuates in blood. CSF ensures the extracellular environment is always at its optimum in terms of constituents to support your brain.

CSF flows through the brain's ventricles. You have four of these: left and right lateral ventricles (which contain most of the CSF); and a third ventricle, which is connected to the fourth by a duct called the cerebral aqueduct. CSF flows around the meninges and spinal cord in an ordered way, before being reabsorbed into the blood by the arachnoid villi (special outgrowths that sit on the arachnoid membrane):

Lateral ventricles → Third ventricle → Cerebral aqueduct → Fourth ventricle → Subarachnoid spaces and bathes brain or spinal cord → Top of brain → Reabsorbed by arachnoid villi

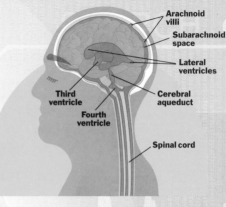

▲ *CSF flows around the brain and spinal cord.*

BLOOD–BRAIN BARRIER

The blood–brain barrier (BBB) deploys modified capillaries, with a highly selective semipermeable endothelial membrane reinforced with tight junctions, that ensure only a few molecules get a 'CSF pass'. Astrocyte foot processes also clasp these capillaries to form a second layer of penetration. The brain couriers in its preferred molecules, such as water, glucose and amino acids, on transport proteins to get its supplies. The choroid plexus and arachnoid epithelium give two extra barriers of protection. By restricting the passage of large water-loving (hydrophilic) molecules into your brain, the BBB protects it from bacteria and various drugs. This is why blood-borne infections of the brain are rare. However, some pathogens do get through by damaging the junctions. Once in, they are difficult to treat because most antibiotics are too large to pass the BBB. Other substances that diffuse through the BBB include the fat-loving (lipophilic) drugs alcohol, caffeine and cocaine.

THE CEREBRUM

There are three main parts of the brain: the cerebrum, brainstem and cerebellum. The cerebrum is the largest part of your brain and the part that makes you human as opposed to an iguana. It is the go-to place for other parts of your brain that need a decision to be made. It is where higher mental processes such as thought, consciousness and memory reside.

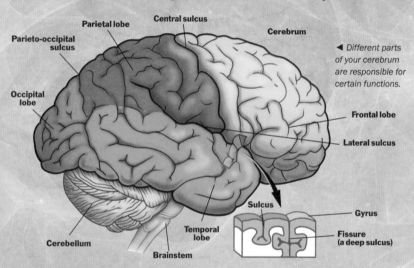

◄ Different parts of your cerebrum are responsible for certain functions.

CEREBRAL CORTEX

The surface of the cerebrum is deeply wrinkled. These folds, or gyri, form the cerebral cortex. From an evolutionary perspective, this 3mm (1/8in) thick layer of grey matter (consisting mostly of cell bodies, synapses and capillaries) symbolizes your highly developed disposition. It is believed that early in our evolution, the brain was very smooth but as we got smarter it needed more space and folded itself (called gyrification) to fit into your skull.

LEFT VS RIGHT

Each hemisphere includes its respective half of the cortex and subcortical regions of the cerebrum. The two hemispheres are joined by a bundle of nerves called the corpus callosum (see page 204) that helps them work together. In terms of motor function, the left hemisphere controls movement on the right side of the body, while the right hemisphere controls movement on the left side. The situation is more complex when it comes to cognitive function. The left brain is logical and analytical, and is associated with practicality, mathematical ability, reasoning and language. The right hemisphere is associated with creativity and feelings, including recognizing faces, intuition, music and art. However, although each hemisphere is essential for eliciting a particular process, the whole brain is needed to realize and optimize a particular cognition.

HEMISPHERES AND LOBES

The gyri are separated by small grooves on the surface called sulci, but some gyri are large and furrow deep into the brain to form fissures. The largest fissure, the medial longitudinal fissure, separates the cerebrum into two halves, the right and left cerebral hemispheres, each of which has fissures dividing it into four lobes. The lobes, which mirror each other in the hemispheres, are the frontal, parietal, occipital and temporal.

BENEATH THE CORTEX

Beneath the cortex is the white matter (so called because it is myelinated) of the cerebrum, mostly made up of support tissue in the form of glial cells and the axons of neurons that transmit nerve impulses in tracts or pathways that connect different areas of the cortex. Various subcortical structures, such as the basal ganglia, thalamus, hypothalamus and hippocampus, occupy the central areas of the cerebrum.

THE HINDBRAIN, MIDBRAIN AND FOREBRAIN

If you slice sideways through a brain, it can be divided into three embryonic regions: hindbrain, midbrain and forebrain, which have distinct functions. These areas formed as swellings in your neural tube as you developed. At the bottom is the hindbrain, consisting of the brainstem and cerebellum.

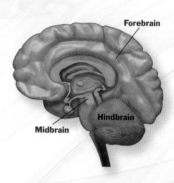

▲ A sagittal view shows the three main regions.

As the eldest of the three areas, in evolutionary terms, the hindbrain has the most important function: keeping you alive. It controls your most essential processes: heart rate, breathing, blood pressure, swallowing, temperature and balance. Structurally, it contains all the brain material you would expect to find in a reptile, which is why it is often referred to as your reptilian brain.

BRAINSTEM

Your brainstem carries out the essential processes, making it the core of your brain. Not only does it link your cerebrum and spinal cord, it also serves as a busy nerve junction, providing the platform for all inbound and outbound nerve signals to pass through. The nerves that connect the right and left hemispheres of your brain also cross over here.

The brainstem plays an important role in keeping you conscious and aware. It also controls all your unconscious functions in centres that regulate your cardiovascular and respiratory systems. For this reason, damage to the brainstem is fatal. The structures in the brainstem that house these centres, including those involved in sleep and feeling awake, are the pons, medulla oblongata and reticular formation (or reticular

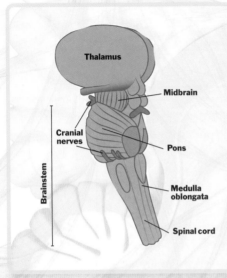

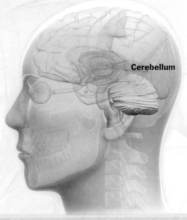

▼ Forming the hindbrain, the brainstem and cerebellum keep you alive.

activating system, which runs thoughout the structure).

CEREBELLUM

At the base of your brain sits a walnut-shell-like structure called the cerebellum, which often gets confused with the cerebrum by virtue of their similar names. The cerebellum, which is Latin for 'little-brain', is the largest structure in your hindbrain. It coordinates your voluntary muscle movements. It also helps you maintain posture and balance by processing impulses received from your sensory systems, such as your inner ear, and coordinating them with your muscles. Unlike the rest of your brain, the cerebellum's left side actually controls the left side of your body. It does this by working with the right hemisphere of your cerebrum.

Injury to the cerebellum can happen if you abuse alcohol or incur damage, as from a stroke or tumour. It is also affected by diseases such as cerebral palsy and multiple sclerosis. The associated symptoms include an unsteady gait, uncoordinated muscle movements, slurred speech and problems performing fine motor tasks.

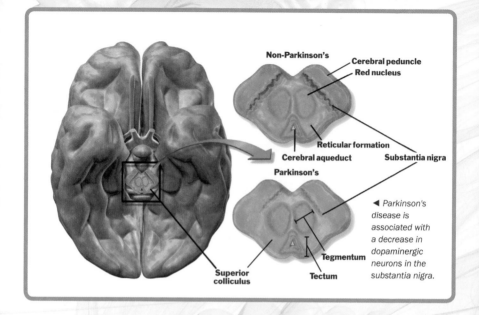

Non-Parkinson's
Cerebral peduncle
Red nucleus
Reticular formation
Cerebral aqueduct
Substantia nigra
Parkinson's
Superior colliculus
Tectum
Tegmentum

◄ *Parkinson's disease is associated with a decrease in dopaminergic neurons in the substantia nigra.*

MIDBRAIN

The midbrain is a small area on top of the brainstem, but it serves a very significant role in connecting the hindbrain with the forebrain. It helps process inbound visual and auditory signals, coordinates movement and manages pain. Important structures include the tectum, tegmentum and cerebral peduncles. These contain a cluster of neurons (referred to as a nucleus in the CNS) that are pigmented and produce the neurotransmitter dopamine. This dark area, referred to as the substantia nigra, is heavily involved in reward and movement.

The death of these dopaminergic neurons results in diseases and syndromes such as Parkinsonism and Parkinson's disease. Increased release of dopamine is thought to be associated with the development of schizophrenia. This is based on evidence that sufferers often respond to drugs that work by blocking the dopamine receptors, and people who use amphetamines that increase levels of dopamine display symptoms similar to schizophrenia. However, there are other theories that challenge this.

FOREBRAIN

This part of the brain is made up of the cerebrum minus the midbrain. Described another way, the forebrain includes the cerebral cortex and underlying subcortical structures such as the thalamus, hypothalamus, basal ganglia and limbic system.

Your cerebral cortex processes information it receives from your five senses. However, it is not just a passive receptacle, as it also sends out commands for other parts of your nervous system to effect. With sensory and motor regions dedicated to specific parts of your body, the four lobes further divide the cortex into functional parts. The sensory areas interpret the information they get from your sense organs, while the motor areas control how and when your skeletal muscles move. Association areas act as go-betweens for the sensory and motor regions. They analyse the sensory information they receive and tweak it before sending it on to specific motor areas.

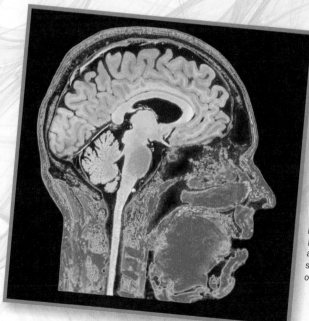

◀ This radiological image shows a sagittal section of the brain, with the different parts clearly visible. In this patient, the cerebral cortex appears thinner and to have shrunk, a classic sign of dementia.

LOBE FUNCTIONS

No one is sure who first said it, but it is often stated: 'If the human brain were simple enough for us to understand, we would be too simple to understand it.' Over the years, significant progress has been made in delineating how your brain and its various lobes are organized and what they do. There is still much to learn as science has only just managed the basics. What is clear is that you exist because it exists; without it there would be no you.

LOBE	DEMARCATING FISSURES	FUNCTION	SPECIFIC CORTEX OR AREAS IT CONTAINS	SPECIFIC FUNCTION
Frontal	Central sulcus (from parietal lobe) Lateral sulcus (from temporal lobe)	Involved in speech, complicated thinking and executing movements (sends commands to the spinal cord and peripheral nerves). It is where your personality resides	Prefrontal cortex	Decision making, social behaviour, personality and higher executive functions
			Premotor cortex	A secondary motor area that helps plan movements and works with other areas to execute coordinated conscious movements
			Primary motor cortex	Helps to initiate and execute coordinated conscious movements. Different parts of the cortex control motor functions of different body areas (see the motor cortical homunculus, page 202)
			Motor speech area (Broca's area)	Helps you form language and control motor functions involved in speech. Damage to this area can cause you to struggle putting words together when you talk
Parietal	Central sulcus Parieto-occipital sulcus	Processes somatosensation: touch, taste, pain and proprioception (information about the position of limbs in space, making use of proprioceptor neurons in tendons and joints)	Primary somatosensory cortex	Receives sensory information from receptors in skin. Different parts of the cortex control sensory functions of different body areas (see the somatosensory cortical homunculus, page 202)
			Somatosensory association area	Integrates information from the primary somatosensory cortex to identify touched objects. Gives awareness of one half of body
			Primary gustatory cortex	Helps you perceive taste: what is sweet, salty, bitter or sour

▶ This lateral view shows the main functional areas of the cerebral cortex. Their key roles are highlighted in the table below.

LOBE	DEMARCATING FISSURES	FUNCTION	SPECIFIC CORTEX OR AREAS IT CONTAINS	SPECIFIC FUNCTION
Occipital	Parieto-occipital sulcus	Helps to process and interpret visual signals to form visual images (other parts of the brain contribute to helping you see)	Primary visual cortex	The major visual processing part of your brain, receiving input from your eyes. Damage to this area results in blindness
			Visual association area	Helps finetune information from the visual cortex. Tries to identify objects and interpret their location, depth and distance
Temporal	Lateral sulcus	Involved in processing and interpreting auditory and olfactory signals, as well as helping process visual information and memory	Primary auditory cortex	The major auditory processing centre, receiving input from your ears and other secondary areas. Damage to this area results in deafness
			Auditory association area	Helps determine whether you are hearing music, someone speaking or other sounds
			Sensory speech area (Wernicke's area)	Involved in helping you understand speech
			Olfactory cortex	Helps you perceive smells

YOU LOOKING AT ME?

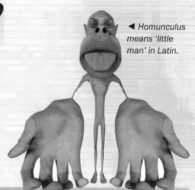

◄ *Homunculus means 'little man' in Latin.*

The image on the right shows how your brain thinks you look. The picture gets no better whichever lens the brain chooses, sensory or motor: you have extremely large hands; a big mouth, tongue and lips; and a small torso, legs and head.

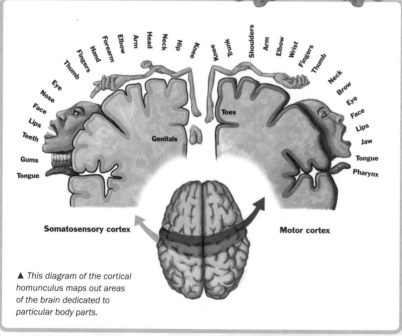

Somatosensory cortex

Motor cortex

▲ *This diagram of the cortical homunculus maps out areas of the brain dedicated to particular body parts.*

The homunculus man was devised by US neurosurgeons Wilder Penfield and Edwin Boldrey, whose work on epileptic patients, published in 1937, enabled them to map various regions of the brain. It depicts how you would look if the amount of cortical space your brain dedicated to different body parts were physically represented. The reason for this distorted self-image is that your brain allocates space in the somatosensory and motor cortexes for processing particular areas based on the extent of their innervation, not the volume of skin or anatomical space they occupy. Those areas of the body blessed with a rich supply of sensory neurons occupy larger areas of the cortex and are consequently more sensitive.

The cortical homunculus is a neurological map that shows areas of the cortex that receive or send information from or to different body areas. These are arranged with the head and associated structures at the bottom of the gyrus while the legs and feet occupy the top. The brain does not have a dedicated area for itself. That is because it does not move or feel sensation. If it did, its 100 billion neurons would send it off the chart!

BLOOD SUPPLY TO THE BRAIN

The paired internal carotid and vertebral arteries supply your brain with blood. The internal carotid arteries feed the anterior, while vertebral arteries feed the posterior. After branching, the vertebral (now known as the basilar) and internal carotid artery meet at the underside of your brain, forming the circle of Willis, a ring of blood vessels that connect at anastomoses to ensure the brain has a backup supply of blood if one of its vessels is blocked or narrowed. Most aneurysms develop in this site and, if they burst, result in brain haemorrhage.

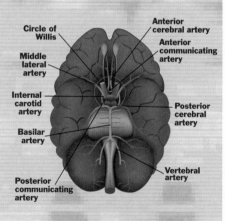

▲ Arterial blood supply to the brain

THE CORPUS CALLOSUM

It makes a C-shape in the middle of your brain and contains up to 300 million nerve fibres all bundled together to ensure that the left hemisphere can communicate with the right. It appears that evolution awarded the corpus callosum only to organisms that received their fetal nourishment directly from their mother via a placenta.

One approach to understanding the roles of structures deep in the brain is finding out how a person functions when these areas are either absent or damaged by trauma and disease. We know what happens if the corpus callosum is unable to function following split-brain surgery in severely epileptic patients, who have had theirs severed in order to control the spread of electrical activity across their brain. One consequence of this palliative procedure is the relative sense of having two separate control centres, often with a loss of awareness of one side of the body, which can act independently from the other. Agenesis of the corpus callosum (ACC) is a

rare condition where people are born without their corpus callosum or with part of it missing or abnormal. These individuals have varying neurological capabilities, with some even going undiagnosed until they have an incidental brain scan. Up until then, they exist as high-functioning adults who may be misconstrued as being slightly lazy or socially awkward.

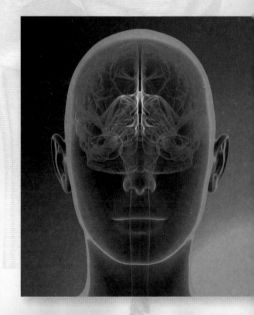

NEW NEURONS

It is estimated that adults lose about 100,000 neurons every day, mostly as a result of ageing. Although it was once thought that adult brains could not synthesize new neurons, research by Dr Maura Boldrini, a neurobiologist at Columbia University, suggests that no matter what your age is, your brain can develop new cells in a process known as neurogenesis. Since nerve cells are incapable of dividing, this suggests that stem cells must exist in the brain. Neurogenesis is thought to happen in your hippocampus (see page 209).

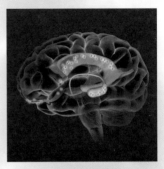

▲ Neurogenesis in an adult human brain is subject to much debate in the scientific world.

In the 20th century it was thought for a while that women had thicker bundles and therefore had much better cross-talk between the two hemispheres than men, which naturally fuelled the belief that women were more intuitive as a result. Subsequent studies have since debunked this generalization, although equipped with the power of current neuroimaging technologies, some studies have revealed that specific parts of the corpus callosum tend to be on average larger in women than in men.

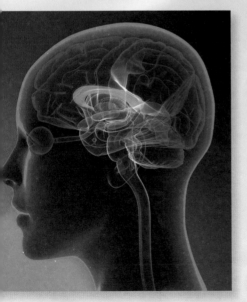

◄ Your corpus callosum looks like a dome and acts like a bridge between your two cerebral hemispheres.

SUBCORTICAL STRUCTURES

The subcortical region encompasses those strangely shaped structures found under the cortex, which includes the diencephalon, limbic system and basal ganglia. These structures intertwine with each other to such an extent that it is no wonder scientists know very little about the brain. To understand what these fascinating structures do is no easy feat, particularly because they dip their fingers in so many pies it sometimes obscures their main role. However, because these structures rely on input from different parts of the brain, it would be inaccurate to suggest that they have a sole function in a particular response.

THE DIENCEPHALON

The diencephalon is a small part of the forebrain that is visible only when the brain is cut in half. It means 'between brain' and forms the wall of the third ventricle. It has multiple functions dictated by the different nuclei (clusters of neuron cell bodies) and structures it contains: the thalamus, hypothalamus, epithalamus and subthalamus.

Thalamus: You have two oval-shaped thalami, sitting on top of the midbrain. The thalamus relays sensory and motor information from the subcortical areas to the cortex for further processing, acting like a telephone exchange system or switchboard. It first routes the signals to specific nuclei contained within the thalamus that can better deal with the information before sending it to the cortex. Sensory

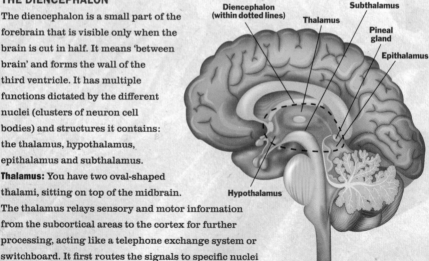

▲ *The diencephalon is seen in this sagittal view of the brain.*

▼ *The reward centres of the brain are primarily based in neural circuits in the cortex, basal ganglia, thalamus and epithalamus.*

Hypothalamus: Covering an almond-sized area, this specialized collection of nerve centres is below the thalamus. The hypothalamus controls the release of hormones from the pituitary gland (endocrine function) and regulates vital functions such as blood pressure, sleep, temperature, hunger and thirst, ensuring homeostasis is maintained. It has links to the pituitary gland, limbic system (see page 208) and autonomic nervous system. Damage to the hypothalamus causes sleep, growth and eating disorders, obesity and diabetes.

Epithalamus: Located behind the thalamus, the epithalamus contains the pineal gland (or body) and habenular nuclei (habenulae). The epithalamus helps connect the limbic system with other parts of the brain, including the basal ganglia. The pineal gland secretes the hormone melatonin, which regulates your biological clock (see pages 234–5). The habenulae are thought to be involved in depression and processing rewards.

Subthalamus: Partly located in the midbrain, the subthalamus contains the subthalamic nucleus. With connections to the basal ganglia and cerebral cortex, the subthalamus modulates skeletal muscle movement. Damage can result in movement disorders, such as irregular violent limb movements.

information from the olfactory system bypasses the thalamus and is routed directly to the cortex. The thalamus is also involved in sleep and consciousness, processing information from the cerebral cortex. As well as having connections to the cerebral cortex, the thalamus is also connected to the hippocampus (see page 208) and basal ganglia (see page 210). Damage or dysfunction in the thalamus results in movement disorders or coma.

THE LIMBIC SYSTEM

The limbic system plays a key role in helping you remember and learn things, controlling your behaviour, and processing your emotional responses including flight or fight. Its connection to the olfactory system explains why a certain smell can evoke memories and trigger emotions. It comprises the following structures:

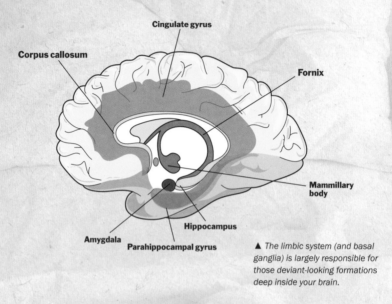

▲ The limbic system (and basal ganglia) is largely responsible for those deviant-looking formations deep inside your brain.

Amygdala: This almond-shaped bulb near the end of the hippocampus is involved in your emotional responses, including fear, anxiety, pleasure and anger. It also hooks emotions to your memories, which helps them become more robust. Damage or dysfunction in the amygdala can result in being less fearful, leading to risk-taking. Other disorders it is associated with include dementia, epilepsy, anxiety and depression.

Hippocampus: There is one hippocampus in each side of your brain. The hippocampus forms the main memory centre and is involved in learning. Damage may cause amnesia, an inability to develop new long-term memories, or forgetting newly gained information. The hippocampus is also believed to be the site of neurogenesis (see page 205).

Cingulate gyrus or cortex: Lying above the corpus callosum and with many connections throughout the brain, the cingulate gyrus helps you modify your behaviour and emotions. Issues with the cingulate gyrus are implicated in psychiatric disorders including schizophrenia, attention deficit disorders and lack of emotional control.

Parahippocampal gyrus or cortex: Situated in the part of the cortex that surrounds the hippocampus, the parahippocampal gyrus helps with spatial processing, recognition of places, putting things in context and modifying your emotions.

Mammillary body: The mammillary bodies are tiny, paired spherical bodies at the ends of the fornix (one in each side of your brain). They act as relay stations that send signals between the thalamus and fornix. Dysfunction results in memory problems.

Fornix: These nerve fibres look like a ram's horns. They are connected to the corpus callosum by the septum pellucidum (thin tissue). They help transmit signals from the hippocampus to the mammillary bodies. Their loss or damage would result in memory problems.

▶ Certain smells can elicit specific memories thanks to the connections made between your hippocampus and olfactory cortex.

THE BASAL GANGLIA

Basal ganglia are not ganglia at all (which are clusters of neurons in the peripheral nervous system). The basal ganglia represent a collection of nuclei that primarily help you form coordinated and smooth movements. These nuclei receive motor plans from the cortex for initiating a particular movement and processes them before sending then back to the cortex (via the thalamus) with information that inhibits any movements that may prevent the planned movement from happening.

Substantia nigra: Although found in the midbrain, the substantia nigra is still part of the basal ganglia. The substantia nigra contains dark-pigmented neurons that produce dopamine (see page 198). This nucleus helps facilitate movement and is thought to be involved in learning and addiction. Dysfunction results in Parkinsonism, a syndrome characterized by impaired speech, movement and posture. Initiating movements can be difficult as well as stopping and sustaining them.

Caudate nucleus: This C-shaped part of the basal ganglia forms part of the striatum, along with the putamen. The caudate nucleus receives information from the cerebral cortex which it modifies and sends back to the cortex via the thalamus. It is believed to be involved in behavioural disorders.

Putamen: While forming the striatum with the caudate nucleus, the putamen also forms the lentiform nucleus together with the globus pallidus. It helps regulate voluntary movement and has a role in behaviour and learning.

▼ Balancing on a unicycle is a skill that requires you having a tip-top vestibular system and basal ganglia.

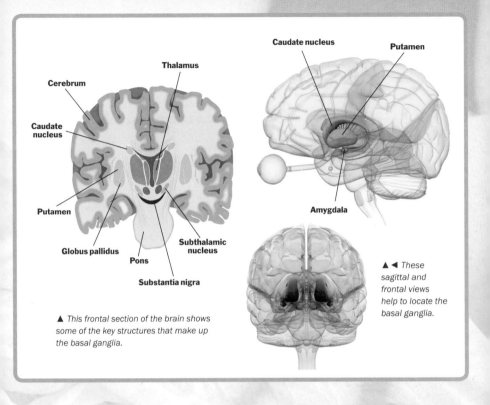

This frontal section of the brain shows some of the key structures that make up the basal ganglia.

▲ ◄ These sagittal and frontal views help to locate the basal ganglia.

The putamen has been linked to several behavioural and psychiatric disorders including Parkinson's disease.

Globus pallidus: This pale spherical area in the basal ganglia helps regulate voluntary movement by inhibiting movements that would prevent correct activity. The nucleus is an alternative target of deep brain stimulation to treat people with Parkinson's disease.

Subthalamic nucleus: This nucleus forms a major part of the subthalamus, where it receives information from the caudate and putamen nuclei (striatum) and helps to modulate the release of dopamine. It also has a possible involvement in cognition. It is the main target area for deep brain stimulation, which is used to treat people suffering from Parkinson's disease.

THE SPINAL CORD

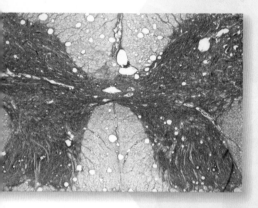

◀ *The anterior and posterior horns of your spinal cord's grey matter are surrounded by white matter.*

GREY MATTER

That central grey matter butterfly is actually a collection of the cell bodies of your neurons. The hind wing, or anterior horn, contains the bodies of motor neurons, while the fore wing, or posterior horn, contains the bodies of sensory and interneurons. In real life, the spinal cord looks pink rather than grey. It has a central canal filled with CSF.

WHITE MATTER

The surrounding white matter is made of bundles of myelinated nerve fibres that group together in nerve tracts running up and down your spine, connecting your brain in both directions. Ascending nerve tracts channel sensory impulses to your brain while those coming down send motor commands to your PNS.

A CENTRAL NERVE SIGNAL HUB

The fibres of these spinal neurons synapse at varying distances along its length with interneurons that relay messages directly to either sensory or motor

It extends from your brain, contains about 1 billion neurons and, depending on your height and gender, is about 40–45cm (16–18in) long. The spinal cord's main function is to act as a two-way communication system between your peripheral nervous system (PNS) and brain. When viewed in the transverse plane, this cylindrical piece of grey and white matter looks rather like a butterfly immersed in a white surround. Just like your brain, it is very well protected, running inside your vertebrae from your brainstem down to your lower back.

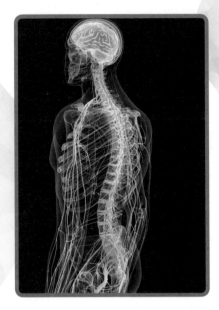

▲ Your spinal cord lives a very comfortable existence in the bones of your back.

neurons. In doing so, sensations detected from around your body are directed to your brain, and effector commands initiated in your brain are able to reach your body tissues. The spinal cord also serves a middle management position, overseeing simple reflexes without any need to disturb the boss upstairs (see page 101). This ensures your brain is not overloaded too much, enabling it to focus its resources on more pressing tasks.

ANATOMY OF A NERVE

A nerve is not the same thing as a neuron, although the latter helps to make up the former. Nerves contain bundles of motor and sensory neurons, or fibres, plus blood vessels and connective tissue. Nerves are constructed a bit like muscles, in that they are arranged into bundles with connective tissue coats covering each structural layer. Each axon fibre is encased in a loose coat of connective tissue called an endoneurium and arranged in a bundle called a fascicle, which itself has its own perineurium jacket. A nerve trunk is a group of fascicles and blood vessels all wrapped up in an outer epineurium.

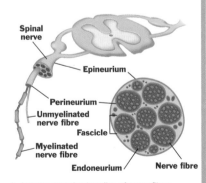

▲ A nerve contains bundles of nerve fibres.

THE 43

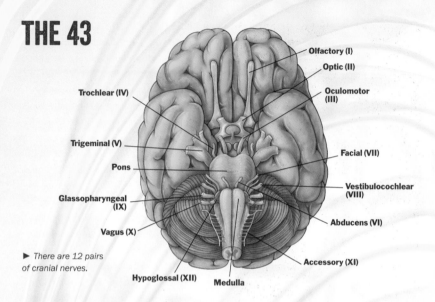

Olfactory (I)
Optic (II)
Oculomotor (III)
Trochlear (IV)
Trigeminal (V)
Pons
Facial (VII)
Glassopharyngeal (IX)
Vestibulocochlear (VIII)
Vagus (X)
Abducens (VI)
Accessory (XI)
Hypoglossal (XII)
Medulla

▶ There are 12 pairs of cranial nerves.

To connect your central nervous system to the rest of your body is no easy feat. As with your cirulatory system, it requires an extensive network of structures capable of branching into every nook and cranny. The peripheral nervous system (PNS) does so through 43 pairs of nerves.

CRANIAL NERVES

Of the 43 pairs of nerves, 12 pairs are cranial nerves, which emerge from the underside of your brain to innervate your sensory organs and the muscles in your head. The exception is pair X, the vagus nerve, which goes down to connect to your airways, heart and digestive system. Some cranial nerves are all motor, some all sensory, and some are a bit of both.

SPINAL NERVES

Your 31 pairs of spinal nerves are carriers of both sensory and motor signals. They innervate the somatic and autonomic divisions of your PNS in areas that fall below your neck. Some band together to form networks of nerves called plexuses. Toward the tail end of your spine, from the second lumbar nerve down, a group of spinal nerves hang loose in the CSF and form tresses that look like a horse's tail and are aptly referred to as your cauda equina.

ROOTS AND BRANCHES

As a nerve travels away from your CNS, the first section is called the nerve root. Cranial nerve roots emerge mostly from the brainstem, except for your olfactory and optical nerves, which travel direct from your cerebrum. Spinal nerve roots emerge from your spinal cord. They have either motor or sensory arms that leave or feed into the anterior and posterior horns of the spinal cord grey matter respectively. Motor nerves leave the spinal cord ventrally, at its front or anterior side. Their sensory counterparts enter the spinal cord dorsally, at the back or posterior side. A mixed spinal nerve forms when both the ventral and dorsal roots combine a bit further away from the spinal cord. It then branches again to form rami, each carrying motor and sensory nerve signals, and continues branching to form networks across your body.

GANGLIA

Ganglia are clusters of neuron cell bodies similar to the nuclei that form in your brain, except they position themselves in various places along your PNS. Sensory, or root, ganglia are found at the dorsal roots of a spinal nerve. Autonomic ganglia (see pages 218–219) form vertical chains that use rami to attach themselves to the spinal nerves, linking the somatic and autonomic systems together.

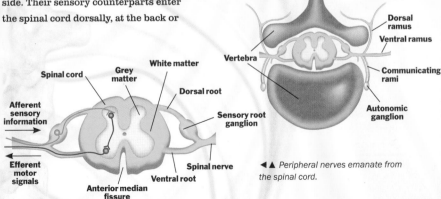

◄ ▲ *Peripheral nerves emanate from the spinal cord.*

IT'S AUTOMATIC

Your peripheral nervous system (PNS) not only has a somatic side, it also has an autonomic side that helps your body do things, such as breathe, without conscious effort. The autonomic nervous system (ANS) is regulated by the hypothalamus.

The somatic division of your PNS is made up of the motor and sensory nerves that connect your brain to your sensory organs, which collect information about the outside world and allow you to make voluntary decisions on how best to respond by way of movement. The ANS is made up of motor, or efferent-only, nerves that mostly emerge from your spine, although some come directly from your brainstem. These nerves innervate the smooth muscle of your blood vessels and your organs, such as heart, lungs, stomach, intestine, bladder and sex organs, as well as your glands.

SYMPATHETIC AND PARASYMPATHETIC

Once the hypothalamus receives information about variations in, for example, your heart rate or blood pressure, it activates appropriate centres in your brainstem (medulla and midbrain) to adjust the ANS and bring your body back into balance. Two parts of your ANS assist with this feedback loop, through their yin and yang relationship dynamic. The sympathetic nervous system gets you all fired up to face any threats and produces fast and speedy responses, to help get you out of tricky situations. In contrast, the parasympathetic nervous system takes its time and serves as your default mode, focusing on the more mundane, non-life-threatening side of life. It either wants you to 'feed and breed' or 'rest and digest'. Although, in reality, the relationship between the two is not as clear cut, they work together to try to achieve balance and homeostasis in your body when things go out of whack.

The enteric nervous system is also sometimes considered part of the ANS. This collection of neurons in your abdomen controls the digestive system and is akin to having an extension of your brain in your guts.

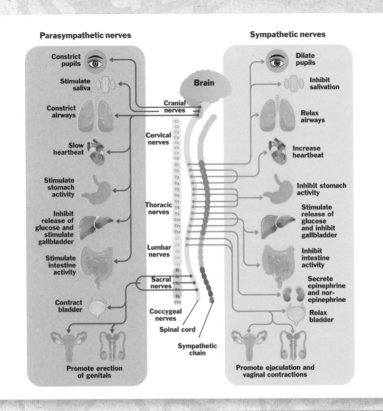

Parasympathetic nerves

Constrict pupils
Stimulate saliva
Constrict airways
Slow heartbeat
Stimulate stomach activity
Inhibit release of glucose and stimulate gallbladder
Stimulate intestine activity
Contract bladder

Brain
Cranial nerves

Cervical nerves
C1 C2 C3 C4 C5 C6 C7 C8
Thoracic nerves
T1 T2 T3 T4 T5 T6 T7 T8 T9 T10 T11 T12
Lumbar nerves
L1 L2 L3 L4 L5
Sacral nerves
S1 S2 S3 S4 S5 Co1
Coccygeal nerves
Spinal cord
Sympathetic chain

Sympathetic nerves

Dilate pupils
Inhibit salivation
Relax airways
Increase heartbeat
Inhibit stomach activity
Stimulate release of glucose and inhibit gallbladder
Inhibit intestine activity
Secrete epinephrine and nor-epinephrine
Relax bladder

Promote erection of genitals

Promote ejaculation and vaginal contractions

SEXUAL AROUSAL

Sympathetic nerves get you fired up, but parasympathetic nerves are responsible for sexual arousal. By dilating your arteries, this allows your penis or clitoral region to expand. (Sympathetic nerves constrict your blood vessels to direct blood to places like your brain that need it more during times of stress.) However, sympathetic neurons do have a role in sex: they are responsible for the ejaculatory orgasm in men.

AUTONOMIC GANGLIA

Autonomic ganglia are different from the sensory ganglia of the somatic division of your PNS. Ganglia arising from the sympathetic nervous system are usually close to the spinal cord, presumably to effect swift changes, and form a chain either side of your spine. In contrast, those of the parasympathetic system are closer to the tissues and organs they innervate.

Autonomic pathways are also different from the efferent pathways of the somatic system. Instead of synapsing directly with their target organ, an autonomic neuron breaks into two segments at the point of their ganglion. The segment between the CNS and the ganglion is called the preganglionic neuron and this synapses with the postganglionic neuron that emerges from the ganglion, on the effector side.

PRE- AND POSTGANGLIONIC NEURONS

Pre- and postganglionic neurons differ in the sympathetic and parasympathetic systems. Sympathetic preganglionic neurons are shorter than parasympathetic ones. The reverse is true of their postganglionic fibres. Both sympathetic and parasympathetic preganglionic

neurons release acetylcholine (ACh) as a neurotransmitter, which binds to nicotinic receptors on the postganglionic neuron to transmit the impulse. However, at the effector side, postganglionic neurons of the sympathetic system release norepinephrine (aka noradrenaline), which binds to adrenergic receptors on the target organ. Postganglionic neurons of the parasympathetic system release ACh, which binds to a different kind of ACh receptor, called a muscarinic receptor, on the target organ.

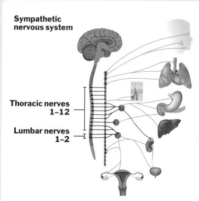

Sympathetic nervous system

Thoracic nerves 1–12

Lumbar nerves 1–2

▲ The sympathetic nerves emerge from the spine (said to have a thoracolumbar outflow) and join the cervical and thoracic spinal nerve pathways to innervate structures in the chest and abdomen. Regions in the head and neck receive innervation via the superior cervical ganglion.

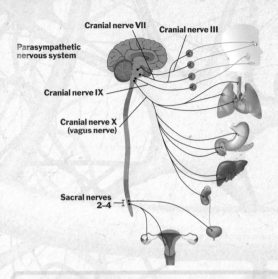

Cranial nerve VII　　Cranial nerve III

Parasympathetic nervous system

Cranial nerve IX

Cranial nerve X (vagus nerve)

Sacral nerves 2–4

◄ *Parasympathetic nerves emerge from the top and tail ends of the spinal column (craniosacral outflow), specifically from the brainstem and lumbar areas that innervate regions in your head (via specific cranial nerves) and pelvis (via specific sacral nerves). The vagus nerve innervates the regions in your chest and abdomen.*

THE ADRENAL GLAND

The adrenal glands perch on top of your kidneys and each is considered to be a modified sympathetic ganglion of sorts. This is because some of its cells are similar to postganglionic neurons. Therefore, when the adrenal gland is stimulated by sympathetic preganglionic neurons, it releases the hormone epinephrine (adrenaline) and norepinephrine (noradrenaline), which spreads into the bloodstream to help optimize the effects of the sympathetic response.

▼ *Your adrenal glands are closely linked to your sympathetic nervous system and play an important role in your fight or flight response.*

Adrenal glands

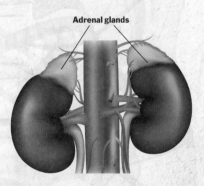

FIVE COMMON SENSES

All your sensory organs, except those of your sense of touch, are in your head, and for good reason. Bypassing the spinal cord allows the information carried in your cranial nerves direct access to the brain for processing. En route to the cerebral cortex, the information passes various subcortical structures, including the limbic system, which sprays a hint of emotion or memory onto what is being sensed.

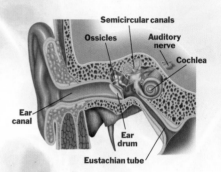

HEARING

Trigger: Sound waves

Sense organ: Ears, which detect the pitch and intensity of sound. The outer ears funnel sound waves into the inner ear. The tympanic membrane (ear drum) vibrates, causing tiny bones in the middle ear, called ossicles, to vibrate. This causes ripples in the fluid contained in a shell-like structure called the cochlea. In addition, your sense of balance arises from the movement of fluid in semicircular canals in your ear, with this information sent to the brain via the vestibular nerve.

Receptors: Auditory receptors, or hair cells, in the cochleas

Nerve: Auditory nerve

Processing centre: Auditory cortex in the temporal lobe

SEEING

Trigger: Light

Sense organ: Eyes, which detect the brightness (intensity) and colour (wavelength) of light entering through the pupil

Receptors: Photoreceptors on the retinas (see page 40)

Nerve: Optic nerve

Processing centre: Visual cortex in the occipital lobe

SMELLING

Trigger: Chemicals

Sense organ: Nose, which detects chemicals dissolved in nasal mucus. Harmful odours can stimulate sneezing.

Receptors: Olfactory receptors (chemoreceptors) in the nasal cavities, which send signals to nerve fibres in the olfactory bulb

Nerve: Olfactory nerve

Processing centre: Olfactory cortex in the temporal lobe

TOUCHING

Trigger: Pressure, vibrations, cold, heat or pain

Sense organ: Skin, especially on the palms of the hands and soles of the feet

Receptors: Meissner's corpuscles in the dermis (see page 63)

Nerve: Spinal and cranial nerves

Processing centre: Somatosensory cortex in the parietal lobe

TASTING

Trigger: Chemicals

Sense organ: Tongue, which detects chemicals dissolved in the fluid of saliva. Input is also received from smell.

Receptors: Gustatory receptors (chemoreceptors) in the taste buds

Nerve: Glossopharyngeal and vagus nerves

Processing centre: Gustatory cortex in the frontal lobe and the insular cortex, between the frontal and temporal lobes

THE MOST IMPORTANT SENSE

It is difficult to decide which is the most important sense, because the answer is subjective. From a purely physiological perspective, if your eye contains the majority of your body's sensory receptors (at least 70 per cent of them), then your sight wins. However, if anecdotal reports from palliative care specialists hold credence, your most treasured senses would be your hearing and touch. These are apparently the last ones you give up before you die.

CHAPTER 9

JUST A MESSENGER

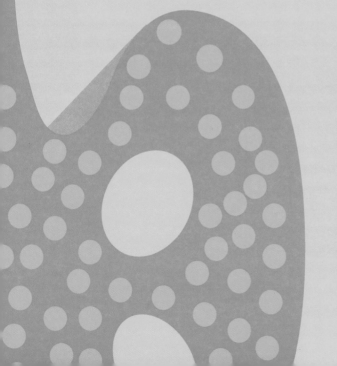

THE ENDOCRINE SYSTEM

There are some things that your body does quietly in the background; that it likes to take its time over because its effects can be life-changing. Your endocrine system is the reason why you transition from a child into an adult, from a girl into a woman, from being awake to falling asleep.

Although your endocrine system has its own primary organs, called endocrine glands, it also borrows some from other systems, sometimes referred to as its secondary organs. All endocrine glands produce chemical messengers called hormones that effect change in their target cell. Primary endocrine organs' main role is to produce hormones, while secondary organs secrete them on the side. The secret to the system's success is the release of its messengers into your bloodstream. Just as advertising companies select their clients based on the size of their fanbase, your endocrine system releases it messages into your blood because it has a captive cellular audience that provides it with access to every cell in your body. Cells that are receptive to the message the hormone carries respond because they have the right receptors on their plasma membrane to receive it.

A negative feedback loop applies the correct adjustment to keep the system stable. The levels of hormones must be tightly controlled as they are very efficacious: a small amount can produce a large effect. By constantly monitoring and adjusting levels of hormones and vital substances in your blood, the system ensures homeostasis is maintained.

Your endocrine system controls or is involved in a wide range of processes:

- Activation of immune T-cells and production of red blood cells
- Childbirth and lactation
- Circadian rhythm and sleep
- Growth
- Hunger
- Menopause and andropause
- Metabolism
- Mood
- Programmed cell death (apoptosis)
- Reproductive cycle
- Sexual development and puberty

ENDOCRINE SYSTEM

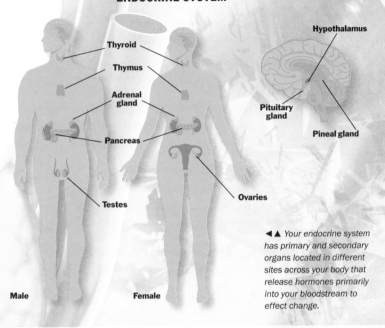

Thyroid

Thymus

Adrenal gland

Pancreas

Testes

Male

Female

Ovaries

Hypothalamus

Pituitary gland

Pineal gland

◄▲ *Your endocrine system has primary and secondary organs located in different sites across your body that release hormones primarily into your bloodstream to effect change.*

FIGHT OR FLIGHT

In addition to directing slow-and-steady processes, the endocrine system does other things relatively fast – because your survival depends on it. Back when man-eating beasts were on the prowl, it was the endocrine system that ensured your ancestors did not become lunch, at least not until they had reproduced. The fight or flight response procures the stimulatory services of your sympathetic nervous system and the subsequent release of the hormones adrenaline and noradrenaline to halt or speed things along.

225

CHEMICAL REVOLUTIONARIES

At least fifty hormones are known to bring about change in your body. They are secreted, usually into the blood, by highly vascularized glands.

TYPES OF SIGNALLING

Hormones communicate with their target cells in several different ways:

Endocrine signalling: This occurs when hormones travel long distances in your blood, far from their secretory homes, before they reach their target cell.

Paracrine signalling: Hormones released in this way act locally and venture only as far as neighbouring cells.

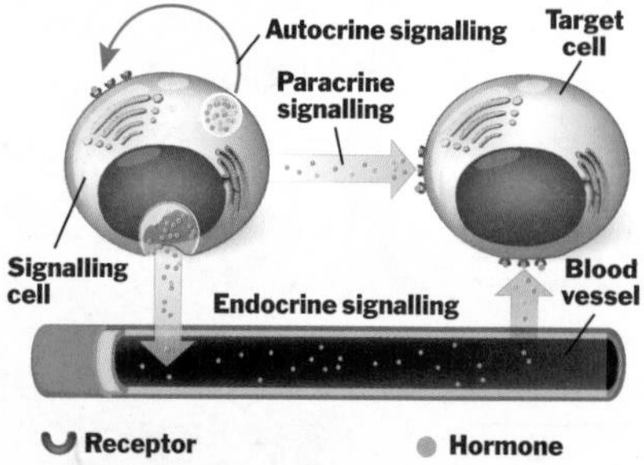

Autocrine signalling: This arises when hormones go as far as the secretory cell's boundary and bind to receptors on the plasma membrane.

Intracrine signalling: Hormones released in this way never leave the confines of the cell as they signal intracellular events.

TARGETING

It is vitally important that target cells carry the right receptors for the hormone to bind to. Receptors are found either on the plasma membrane of the target cell or patiently floating inside the cell in the cytoplasm, waiting to meet that stimulating hormonal partner of theirs. Various endocrine diseases and disorders arise if: hormones fail to attach to their specific receptors; hormones initiate a response in a target cell that is already coupled; the target cell has mutated receptors that respond in an abnormal way; or the target cell gets attacked by autoimmune cells.

MAIN CLASSES OF HORMONES

Steroids are a class of hormones that bind with receptors in the cell cytoplasm. They are fat soluble so that they can

▼ Endocrine signalling is the main way that hormones of the endocrine system work.

Autocrine signalling
Paracrine signalling
Target cell
Signalling cell
Endocrine signalling
Blood vessel
Receptor
Hormone

easily pass through the target cell's membrane and bind to its intracellular receptors. Once bound, they travel as a unit to the nucleus, where they activate a specific gene to start making particular proteins.

The most common type of hormones are those that are made of short chains of amino acids called peptides. Because they love water (are hydrophilic), their receptors exist on the outside of the cell as they cannot pass through the membrane. Once bound to receptors, this activates a second messenger inside the cell, usually a molecule called cyclic adenosine monophosphate (cAMP) that is responsible for initiating the intracellular events on the hormone's behalf.

Amine hormones are derived from amino acids called tryptophan or tyrosine. They include the catecholamines adrenaline and noradrenaline that initiate your fight or flight response.

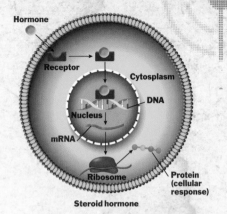

Steroid hormone

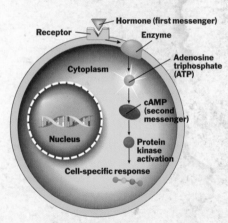

Non-steroid hormone

▶ *Steroidal and non-steroidal hormones induce cellular responses in different ways.*

CLASS	EXAMPLES	SECRETORY GLAND
Steroids (fat soluble)	Testosterone / Oestrogen	Secreted in both sexes by the adrenal gland (cortex) and gonads of the reproductive system
Peptides (hydrophilic)	Glucagon	Secreted by the pancreas and binds to glucagon receptors on the surface of liver cells. Activation initiates events inside liver cells that cause glycogen conversion to glucose.
Amines	Adrenaline / Noradrenaline	Secreted by the adrenal gland (medulla)

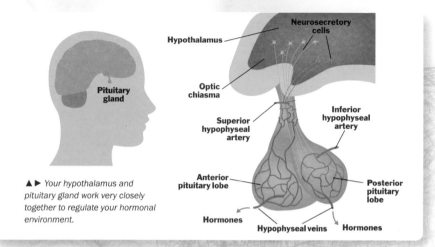

Hypothalamus

Neurosecretory cells

Optic chiasma

Superior hypophyseal artery

Inferior hypophyseal artery

Pituitary gland

Anterior pituitary lobe

Posterior pituitary lobe

Hormones

Hypophyseal veins

Hormones

▲ ▶ *Your hypothalamus and pituitary gland work very closely together to regulate your hormonal environment.*

KNOW YOUR GLANDS

As mentioned before, some endocrine glands are considered primary, or major, while others have secondary status by virtue of their other functions and control. Here is a close up of a few of them.

MAJOR ENDOCRINE GLANDS

Hypothalamus: This is the structure that links your nervous and endocrine systems together. The hypothalamus is the one in charge of most hormones and sits in the centre of the brain just above its work buddy, the pituitary gland. It sends instructions to the pituitary gland to either start or stop secreting hormones that target the rest of your body. It controls your temperature, thirst, hunger and circadian rhythms.

Pituitary gland: This gland looks like two peas and is attached to the hypothalamus via a stalky structure. It is the endocrine puppet master for it directly controls the function of other glands in your body, and how you grow and develop.

It has two lobes with different roles. The anterior (front) lobe is where it releases its hormones, such as luteinizing, follicle-stimulating, thyroid-stimulating and adrenocorticotropic hormones. These stimulate other hormone-secreting structures, including your reproductive organs and adrenal glands. The anterior lobe also releases growth hormones that stimulate the development or maintenance of your bone and muscle mass. The posterior (back) lobe stores hormones it receives from the hypothalamus, such as oxytocin and anti-diuretic hormone (ADH; aka vasopressin), which are released as and when needed. Oxytocin, also known as the love hormone, plays a key role during and after childbirth, while ADH targets your kidneys to prevent water loss and your blood vessels to help regulate blood pressure.

▲ Oxytocin hormone helps with social bonding. It is secreted by the pituitary gland during and after childbirth, and is also released during a cuddle.

Pineal gland or body: This is tucked in the middle of your brain, in the epithalamus (see page 207). Those of a spiritual persuasion believe this small gland is where your soul resides, 'the third eye'. What is clear from science is that the pineal gland secretes the sleep hormone melatonin when the light hitting your eyes decreases.

Thymus: This organ occupies prime position in the top centre of your chest. It is perched just above your heart and cradled between your lungs. This lymphoid organ has historically been considered to be part of the endocrine system by virtue of the fact that it secretes the hormone thymosin that triggers the development and production of immune cells called T-lymphocytes. However, there is currently some debate as to whether it is an endocrine organ. It is very active and large during childhood and shrinks as you get older.

Adrenal glands: These two glands sit on top of both your kidneys like little Persian hats. Each gland has an outer cortex that is about 2cm (⁴/₅in) thick and an inner medulla. This particular endocrine organ is known as the fight or flight gland because it controls how you react under stressful situations. Your sympathetic nerves stimulate the medulla to release the amine hormones adrenaline and noradrenaline that bolster the sympathetic response: the medulla essentially converts signals from your sympathetic nervous system into hormonal ones. The adrenal cortex, on the other hand, produces small amounts of the steroid hormones oestrogen and testosterone, plus aldosterone and cortisol. The latter, known as the stress hormone, is released under fight or flight conditions and has a range of metabolic functions, including suppressing inflammation. It naturally rises if you do little exercise or have a poor diet, which if prolonged can dampen your immune system. Your adrenal glands also help regulate your blood pressure and how much fat you burn.

Thyroid: Not to be confused with the thymus, this double-lobed structure, which resembles a mini bow tie clasped firmly onto your windpipe, is centrally controlled by the hypothalamus and the anterior lobe of the pituitary gland. It helps maintain your metabolism (the conversion of oxygen, fats and sugars from food into energy) by releasing iodine-derived hormones T3 and T4 (thyroxine). These regulate processes such as your growth, and whether cells should store or metabolize glucose to release energy. The pituitary gland regulates thyroid activity by releasing thyroid stimulating hormone (TSH). If thyroid hormones are too low, the hypothalamus instructs the pituitary gland to release TSH so that it produces more T3 and T4. Various disorders arise if your thyroid gland is over- or underactive. Too much thyroid hormones (hyperthyroidism) results in excess sweating, weight loss, rapid pulse, bulging eyes and heat intolerance.

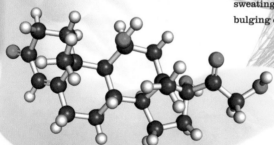

◀ This is the molecular structure of the stress hormone cortisol, which helps to control blood pressure and regulates the metabolism of glucose. However, exposure to too much cortisol over prolonged periods can cause serious health problems.

Too little thyroid hormones (hypothyroidism) causes thinning and balding hair, fatigue, puffy face, slow heartbeat, weight gain and cold sensitivity.

Parathyroid: There are four of these tiny glands, two on the posterior part of each lobe of the thyroid gland. They control calcium levels in your blood and bones, which must be tightly regulated to prevent serious problems. Parathyroid hormones (PTH) are released in response to low blood calcium levels and act on the kidneys and small intestines to reabsorb or absorb more calcium respectively. PTH enlists vitamin D, which is converted in the kidneys to its active form and travels to the small intestine, where it aids formation of calcium-binding proteins. PTH also stimulates osteoclasts in the bone to break down bone tissue and release calcium into the blood. If levels of blood calcium are too high, the thyroid gland steps in and releases the hormone calcitonin, which facilitates the storage of calcium in your bones.

Pancreas: This leaf-shaped organ hides behind your stomach, with its head and body mid-centre and its tail veering toward the left side of your upper abdomen. The pancreas sits on top of the main artery to the spleen and has a rich capillary network. It has both endocrine and exocrine functions, with the latter involved in digestion (see pages 247 and 250). The pancreas's role as an endocrine gland is governed by a tiny proportion of cells arranged in clusters called islets of Langerhans. These clusters contain alpha and beta cells that help regulate

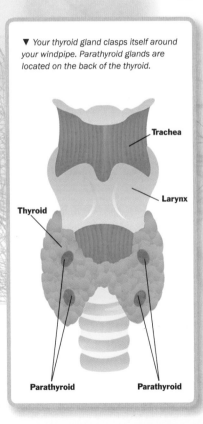

▼ Your thyroid gland clasps itself around your windpipe. Parathyroid glands are located on the back of the thyroid.

Trachea

Larynx

Thyroid

Parathyroid

Parathyroid

the level of sugar in your blood. Alpha cells secrete glucagon, which targets liver cells to release more sugar into the blood, while beta cells secrete insulin, which has the opposite effect, causing the liver to convert glucose to glycogen for storage, as well as encouraging glucose uptake in cells. Diabetes, characterized by high blood sugar levels, broadly arises when the pancreas either does not produce enough insulin (Type I) or your body does not respond to the insulin that is produced (Type II). The former is an autoimmune issue in which the body destroys beta cells, while the latter is a metabolic disorder often associated with being overweight and/or having a bad diet. When your pancreas is inflamed, called acute pancreatitis, it causes a sharp pain in the upper abdomen. This is distinct from the low-grade symptoms of pancreatic cancer, which are often diagnosed at a late stage.

Ovaries: Women have two of these, one on either side of their pelvis. These gonads are stimulated by luteinizing and follicle-stimulating hormones secreted from the anterior pituitary gland. Ovaries produce the hormones oestrogen and progesterone, which control a woman's sexual development, menstrual cycle, pregnancy and childbirth. Testosterone is also among the hormones produced. Too much testosterone production could result in polycystic ovarian syndrome, which can affect reproductive health and alter appearance. For more on the ovaries, see pages 280–81.

Testes: Men have two of these, which sit outside the body in their own sac as they need to be a couple of degrees lower than normal body temperature to aid sperm production.

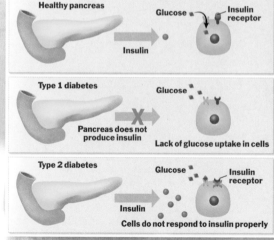

◄ Diabetes is a condition that causes your blood sugar levels to be high. There are two main types that arise: Type I and Type II.

▶ This simplified flow diagram shows how hunger and satiety hormones interact with each other. After eating, the metabolic hormone incretin is released by the small intestine and increases insulin secretion from the pancreas. Insulin can cause target cells to increase glucose uptake (in addition to glycogenesis in the liver). Ghrelin released by the stomach stimulates appetite.

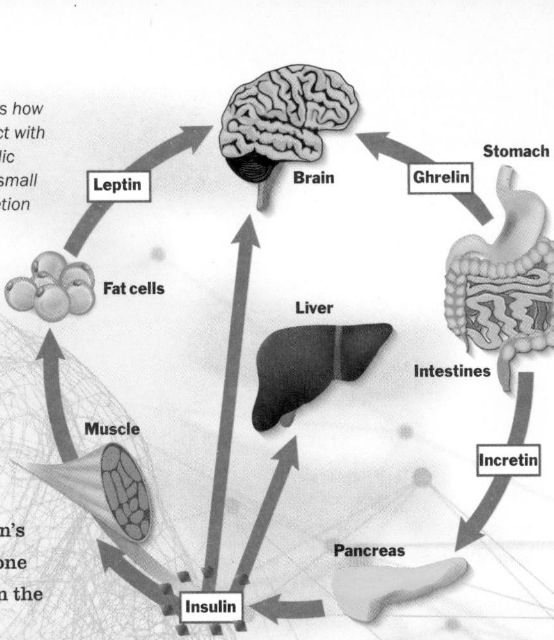

These glands secrete testosterone, which drives sexual development and a man's libido as well as increasing bone and muscle mass. For more on the testes, see pages 276–7.

SECONDARY ENDOCRINE ORGANS

Heart: Your heart is more than just a pump: it also releases hormones. The atria secrete atrial natriuretic peptide (ANP), which encourage the kidneys to lose water to help reduce the volume of your blood and subsequently your blood pressure.

Stomach: G cells that line part of your stomach secrete gastrin when the stomach gets food or is stretched. Gastrin triggers neighbouring parietal cells to secrete gastric acid.

Kidneys: Remarkably, your kidneys actually play a significant role in respiration. By secreting the hormone erythropoietin in response to low levels of oxygen in the blood, this stimulates the production of red blood cells in your bone marrow.

Fat: Leptin is one of the hormones secreted by fat. Leptin tells your brain if fat levels are rising or falling, so your brain has an idea of its energy stores. Leptin stops you feeling hungry by inhibiting the appetite centres in your hypothalamus responsible for hunger, and stimulating those responsible for making you feel full.

SLEEPY HEAD

It is not completely understood why you sleep, but theories include that it consolidates your memories into the long term, it saves energy, it cleans and restores your brain, and even that it evolved to keep you safe from night-time predators. What is clear is that, without sleep, you would not last very long. You spend about a third of your life asleep, which means if you are 70 years old, you have been asleep for just over 23 years.

Sleep is the best medicine you will ever get. You need it whatever your age, although the required dose varies according to each individual and reduces with age. It must be taken with care as its quality varies considerably. It should always be taken at night, preferably 3 to 4 hours after food, but can be taken in small doses throughout the day if needed. Alcohol can affect its efficacy, so you are best advised to reduce your consumption. Failure to take it regularly could affect your mood, cause weight gain and lead to serious withdrawal symptoms and adverse effects such as cognitive and memory impairment, increased blood pressure and risk of heart disease. The risk of ill-effects from overdose are limited, but consult your physician if you find you are constantly in need of taking more than the recommended dosage as this may indicate an underlying condition.

CIRCADIAN RHYTHM
Sleep is controlled by a hormone cycle called the circadian rhythm, a body clock that regulates how sleepy and awake you feel. It exists in your hypothalamus as

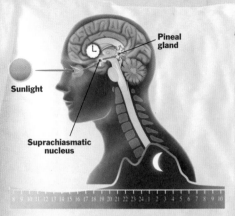

Pineal gland

Sunlight

Suprachiasmatic nucleus

STAGES OF SLEEP

There are five stages of sleep, which can be divided into two phases: non-rapid eye movement (NREM) and rapid eye movement (REM). NREM comprises 75–80 per cent of your sleep and includes a phase where deep sleep occurs, which is associated with the release of growth hormones from the pituitary gland that help your body repair and cells reproduce. Most of your dreams take place during REM. Luckily, your body paralyses your muscles during this phase to avoid you acting them out. REM usually lasts about 90 minutes at a time, there being several cycles of REM and NREM each night.

the suprachiasmatic nucleus (SCN), a structure situated just near where the optic nerves cross each other. The clock, which is set on a 24-hour timescale, is calibrated by the amount of sunlight that hits your eye, particularly blue light. This light is detected by special receptors in your eyes called photosensitive retinal ganglion cells, which feed back to the SCN and pineal gland. The SCN then suppresses production of the sleep hormone melatonin by the pineal gland, which causes you to wake up.

Blue-light emitting devices such as computers, TVs and smartphones can interfere with your body clock and cause sleep disorders, such as insomnia, a condition that most people experience at some point.

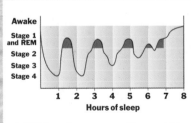

▲ REM (in red) occurs several times a night.

235

GETTING HOT IN HERE

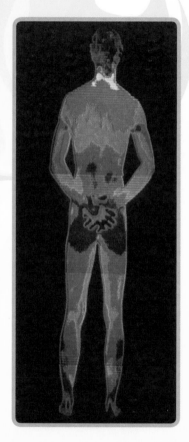

▲ A thermogram, using an infrared camera, detects heat distribution and blood flow in your tissues.

Have you ever thought about the source of your body heat, the location of that elusive internal boiler? In truth, there is no single inner furnace. You are warmed by the collective effort of all your body processes, especially those arising in very active deep organs like your liver, heart and brain, as well as by movement of your skeletal muscles.

Heat is the byproduct of generating energy to fuel all your physiological processes. This energy comes in the form of adenosine triphosphate (ATP), which is produced along with heat when your cells metabolize fats and sugars. Heat is also released when these processes use up this energy to perform their duties.

In a sense, every cell in your body is like a little stove, generating cell-sized pots of heat. The rate at which this occurs is governed by the hypothalamus. As your body's thermostat, it likes to keep things set at 37°C (98.6°F). This is the optimum temperature for the work of your enzymes and biological molecules. A degree higher or lower is tolerable, but dare to venture outside these margins and you are on course for a complete shutdown.

For this reason, our trusty hypothalamus uses its sensors to respond to temperature fluctuations and initiates control mechanisms that either increase or decrease the production or dissipation of energy to return the temperature to its normal settings.

◀ *Diving into icy water causes your hypothalamus to stimulate your thyroid and adrenal glands (via your pituitary gland) with the intention of increasing your metabolic rate to generate heat.*

Being an endothermic animal means you are able to maintain your core temperature at a constant level regardless of your external temperature. The trade-off is that you must eat at regular intervals to ensure there is a continual supply of raw materials to burn.

HYPOTHERMIA

Hypothermia arises when your body temperature drops below 35°C (95°F). Your hypothalamus sends impulses to different effectors to adjust body temperature. It hormonally thermoregulates your body by stimulating your thyroid and adrenal glands to secrete thyroxine and adrenaline to increase the metabolic rate and generate heat. Your autonomic nervous system kick-starts changes that conserve heat, such as vasoconstriction of blood vessels to divert heat in your blood away from your skin and toward more vital organs, causing pallor; and involuntary contraction and relaxation of your muscles (shivering) to burn fuel

and generate heat. If the cold prolongs, the body's processes begin to slow down as nerve impulses become sluggish, heart and breathing rate slows and confusion sets in. At temperatures lower than 32°C (89.6°F), emergency intervention is necessary as you stop shivering and begin to drift out of consciousness. Below 30°C (86°F), death is likely, as your body no longer has the capacity to warm itself.

HYPERTHERMIA

Hyperthermia arises when your body temperature reaches higher than 37.5–38.3°C (99.5–100.9°F). At this temperature, you sweat profusely; your blood pressure drops due to loss of fluid, which makes you liable to fainting, headaches and thirst; and blood is routed to your skin and vessels expand to release heat, causing flushing. If body temperature rises above 40°C (104°F), macromolecules such as proteins are close to the point of denaturing. If they can no longer function, this could lead to cell death and multiple organ failure.

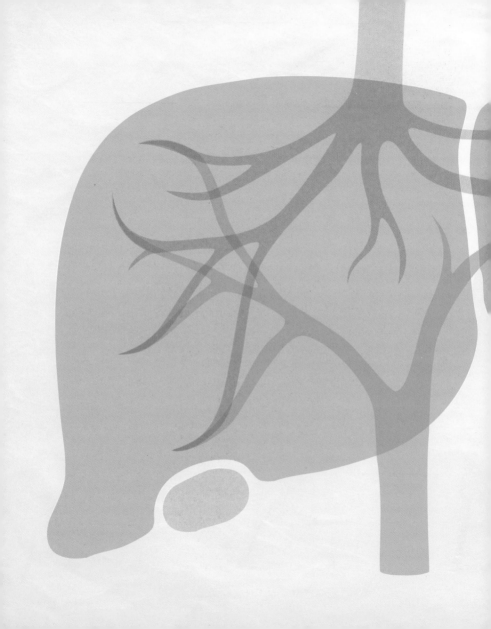

CHAPTER 10

DIGESTING IT ALL

THE DIGESTIVE SYSTEM

It has several different monikers linked to it, but your digestive system is the umbrella term for your gastrointestinal tract (GIT), or alimentary canal and its associated accessory organs. The GIT is the ultimate alchemist as it skilfully breaks food down into essential component parts, or nutrients, that your body uses either to make energy or as raw materials.

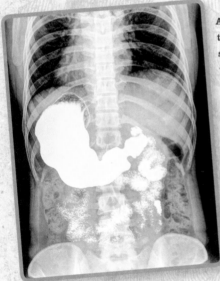

▲ Your gastrointestinal tract can be viewed using a barium swallow test. This special type of X-ray enables doctors to visualize the upper portions of your GIT.

At about 9m (30ft) long, your GIT clearly takes the business of digestion very seriously. It provides the passageway through which food enters and travels through your body, where it is stripped of its nutrients before being expelled as something smelly and undesirable.

UPPER AND LOWER GIT

The GIT can be split into two divisions: the upper and lower GIT. The upper GIT comprises the mouth (and its accessory structures, the teeth, salivary glands and tongue), pharynx, oesophagus (foodpipe), stomach and first part of the small intestine, called the duodenum. Accessory organs and tissues that help with the work of the upper GIT are the liver, pancreas, gallbladder and bile ducts. The lower GIT is made up of the remaining parts of the small intestine (jejunum and ileum) and the large intestine, which includes the caecum, appendix, colon, rectum and anal canal.

DIGESTIVE SYSTEM

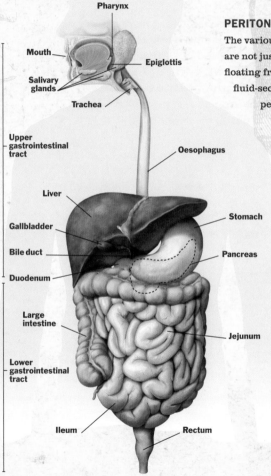

Pharynx

Mouth

Salivary glands

Epiglottis

Trachea

Upper gastrointestinal tract

Oesophagus

Liver

Gallbladder

Stomach

Bile duct

Pancreas

Duodenum

Large intestine

Jejunum

Lower gastrointestinal tract

Ileum

Rectum

PERITONEUM

The various organs and tissues of the GIT are not just submerged in your abdomen floating freely. They are embedded in a fluid-secreting membrane called the peritoneum and are also attached to the back of the abdominal wall by a fan-like structure called the mesentery.

The mesentery is formed by a double fold of peritoneum. Together these structures allow your guts to move freely against each other without friction while firmly holding them in place. They also provide a conduit for the blood vessels, lymphatic vessels and nerves to supply the intestines.

◄ *Your digestive system is essentially one long pipe that has several accessory organs attached to it. Specific tasks are delegated to different regions and structures.*

IN YOUR MOUTH

Your mouth serves several functions: it is the entrance to your digestive tract and lungs, as well as facilitating speech, so it is important that oral activities are finely tuned and coordinated. In short, eating requires mastery of the structures in your mouth. After food leaves your oral cavity and is swallowed, it is no longer under your conscious control.

HUNGER

The road to digestion starts before food enters your mouth. When your stomach is empty, it secretes the hormone ghrelin, which binds to receptors in the hypothalamus and triggers hunger pangs. While on the prowl for food, the mere sight or smell of it can also stimulate your salivary glands into action via a parasympathetic conditioned reflex that causes you to salivate.

TEETH

The first step when eating is to mechanically break down the food with your teeth and chew it to a pulp. By the time you reach adulthood, you have a set of 32 of these hard bone-like structures, which implant themselves into your jaws

▼ *This diagram shows the adult teeth and the average age at which they erupt in years. You have five types, differing in shape, size and function.*

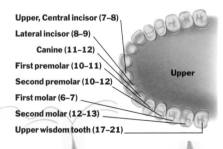

Upper, Central incisor (7–8)
Lateral incisor (8–9)
Canine (11–12)
First premolar (10–11)
Second premolar (10–12)
First molar (6–7)
Second molar (12–13)
Upper wisdom tooth (17–21)

Upper

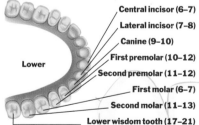

Lower

Central incisor (6–7)
Lateral incisor (7–8)
Canine (9–10)
First premolar (10–12)
Second premolar (11–12)
First molar (6–7)
Second molar (11–13)
Lower wisdom tooth (17–21)

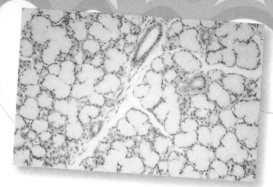

▶ This histological section of a salivary gland shows clusters of secretory cells (acini). These exocrine cells produce either mucous or serous fluid, which drains into the various ducts.

from the inside out. They are coated with the hardest material in your body, enamel, which makes them tough. They vary in shape and size according to whether they tear or grind. The vagaries of your diet can determine the extent to which you lose enamel, exposing the sensitive calcified dentine core and dental pulp to damage and infection.

SALIVA

As you chew, the food is mixed with saliva secreted by the salivary glands. This helps to moisten dry food, which is necessary for you to taste it, as your taste buds can only respond to food that is dissolved in liquid. However, saliva is more than just a wet lubricant: it also serves to chemically digest food and disinfect it. This is because it also contains the enzyme amylase, which digests complex carbohydrates like starch, and the antimicrobial enzyme lysozyme.

Different salivary glands secrete different types of saliva. The largest gland is the parotid, in front of and slightly below the ear, which produces watery saliva. It is the main exocrine gland to secrete amylase. The submandibulars secrete the most saliva, containing a lot of mucus and amylase. Your mouth is also lined with mucous membrane that secretes mucus to keep it moist.

TONGUE

Eating would not be possible without that pink mound of tissue inside your mouth. Your tongue is composed mostly of muscle that runs in different directions. This allows it to toss and mould the food being eaten, pressing it against the hard palate (roof of the mouth) and presenting it either to the teeth or back of the throat for swallowing. It is connected to the floor of your mouth by a thin strip of tissue called the frenulum and at the back to your lower jaw.

DOWN THE PIPE

Once you swallow, you have committed food to the part of your GIT that you no longer control. A deliberate and active process takes hold, channelling food direct to the stomach, irrespective of whether gravity is on its side or not. This makes swallowing food while standing on your head a real – albeit uncomfortable – possibility.

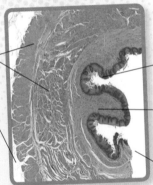

Muscular layer: Circular and longitudinal smooth muscle fibres that contract and pulse food down

Adventitia: Outer protective layer of fibrous connective tissue

Mucosal layer: An inner layer of stratified epithelium that secretes mucus that enables food to pass easily

Submucosal layer: Connective tissue that holds the oesophagus in place

Lumen: Where food passes

SWALLOWING

When the muscles of your pharynx contract, a bolus of food is sent to the upper region of the oesophagus. The tongue is raised to the roof of the mouth as the soft palate descends to close off the space at the back of the nose called the nasopharynx. Your soft palate, which is a flap of non-bony tissue at the back of your mouth near your pharynx,

▲ *A histological section of the oesophagus shows the different layers that it contains.*

is there to prevent food from going up into your nose – although it does not always manage it, as you might have experienced while drinking and laughing. The epiglottis that seals the windpipe is forced shut. All of this is highly coordinated because swallowing and breathing are mutually exclusive: doing both at the same time is prohibited because it would make you choke.

OESOPHAGUS

The oesophagus is an elastic muscular tube that tilts slightly to the left and is positioned behind your trachea. It is about 25cm (10in) long and, before it connects with the stomach, it passes through the diaphragm like a straw pushed through the lid of a disposable milkshake cup. If the oesophageal sphincter were absent, acidic fluid from the stomach would flow into the lower part of the oesophagus, causing continuous acid reflux and inflammation. Some people develop a mucosal tissue called a Schatzki ring that narrows the oesophagus and causes the sensation of food being trapped, especially after eating bread and meat.

The oesophagus does not just let food slide or plop down to the stomach, but rather elegantly pulses food along in a wavelike motion through a process called peristalsis, which occurs throughout the GIT.

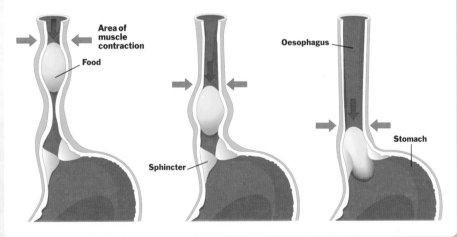

▼ Food travels down your oesophagus in a wave-like motion. This movement, known as peristalsis, involves the sequential contraction and relaxation of the smooth muscle layer.

Area of muscle contraction

Food

Oesophagus

Sphincter

Stomach

DIGESTION TAG-TEAM

Amazingly, and quite disturbingly, your abdomen contains organs capable of digesting you from the inside out. Your stomach and duodenum have each other's back. The first is predominately an acidic secretor, while the latter is mostly alkaline – but both work together to get the job done: digestion.

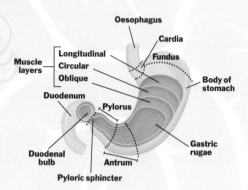

▲ The muscular layers of the stomach orientate themselves in different directions to help churn the food as much as possible.

STOMACH

Your stomach is a muscular J-shaped sac. It connects your oesophagus to the upper part of the small intestine, or duodenum. Like other parts of the digestive system, its muscles are arranged in different directions, which helps it churn food. This food reservoir breaks down what you ingest by virtue of its epithelial lining, which contains glands and cells that secrete the gastric juice that contains the bug-busting and protein-degrading substance hydrochloric acid. Cells in the stomach also secrete mucus, which provides a physical barrier that protects the stomach from ingesting itself, plus bicarbonate, which helps control acidity.

The lining also rather cleverly produces inactive (zymogen) forms of digestive enzymes that become stimulated or active only in acidic environments. The protease pepsinogen is transformed to its active form, pepsin, which begins breaking down proteins. Lipase begins the process of breaking down fatty substances. After a few hours, the partially digested food forms soup-like chyme, which trickles past the gatekeeping pyloric sphincter into the duodenum, where the process of digestion is ramped up many notches.

DUODENUM

The first part of the small intestine curls around the head of the pancreas. It is about 25cm (10in) and affixed to the back of the abdominal wall. When you think of the small intestine, absorption rather than digestion springs to mind. However, the former can occur in any part of the GIT from the stomach (where alcohol, medications such as aspirin and some water are absorbed into the bloodstream) onward, but the next stage of digestion takes place in the duodenum. Its innermost mucosal layer produces an alkaline secretion that contains digestive enzymes and also secretes mucus to prevent erosion. The duodenum receives digestive enzymes produced by the pancreas and bile from the liver that enter via the common bile duct. Their alkaline pH also helps to neutralize the acidity of the chyme.

PANCREAS PRODUCTION

As part of its exocrine function, the pancreas produces different enzymes that have specific degradative roles. They are released in zymogen form and activated by an enzyme lining the duodenum.

PANCREATIC ENZYME	EXAMPLE (ACTIVE FORM)	TARGETS	BREAKDOWN PRODUCTS
Carbohydrases	Amylase	Carbohydrates	Simple sugars
Proteases	Pepsin and trypsin	Proteins	Amino acids
Lipases	Steapsin	Fats and oils	Fatty acids and triglycerides

▶ The pancreas produces the bulk of digestive enzymes that form an alkaline juice in the duodenum. They travel down the pancreatic duct to enter the duodenum.

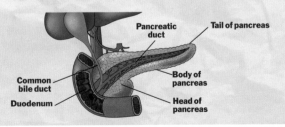

Pancreatic duct

Tail of pancreas

Common bile duct

Body of pancreas

Head of pancreas

Duodenum

THE LIVER

It feels sacrilegious to refer to your liver as an accessory organ, because it is almost a system in itself. The hepatobiliary system includes the liver, gallbladder and bile ducts. The liver is the largest visceral organ you have, and you cannot live without it.

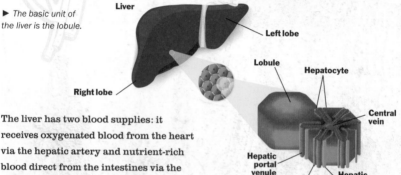

▶ *The basic unit of the liver is the lobule.*

The liver has two blood supplies: it receives oxygenated blood from the heart via the hepatic artery and nutrient-rich blood direct from the intestines via the hepatic portal vein. The liver is the first organ to receive the latter because its job is to sort through what has been absorbed into the blood before allowing it to go back to the heart and circulate to the lungs and around the body.

This brownish red organ, tucked underneath the diaphragm and partially protected by the right lower ribcage, is formed of two lobes, left and right, with the latter being the largest. Each contains thousands of hexagonal lobules that are surrounded by blood vessels.

At each corner of a lobule is a trio of vessels comprising the venules and arterioles of the incoming hepatic portal vein and hepatic artery, plus a bile duct that merges into larger hepatic ducts that leave the liver en route to the duodenum. The centre of each lobule contains an outpouring vein that merges into the interlobular vein and hepatic vein and takes the processed and deoxygenated blood to the heart.

HEPATOCYTES

Each lobule contains thousands of liver cells known as hepatocytes. These are the main workers in this factory that processes, manufactures and stores substances the body needs, might need or does not want. Other cells include the phagocytic Kupffer cells that destroy worn-out or excess red blood cells and any bacteria. Hepatocytes also produce bile, which travels across the lobules in canaliculi that drain into bile ducts that transport it for storage in the gallbladder. Bile is a bitter green liquid that is released from the gallbladder to help digest fats that enter the duodenum.

REGENERATION

The liver is so important that it is one of the few organs that can regenerate itself after damage. This is necessary partly because it is constantly dealing with toxic substances. However, if the assault it receives is continuous so that it has no time to repair itself before the next onslaught, scarring is inevitable. This results in cirrhosis, a condition that causes all sorts of problems and increases the risk of liver cancer.

A LIVER'S WORK

The liver sorts compounds such as:

- Toxic chemicals and waste, neutralizing them and sending them to the kidneys
- Ammonia, which is formed during the breakdown of proteins and is metabolized into a harmless waste product called urea, which gets excreted in your urine, sweat and tears

The liver makes:

- Glucose, from stores of glycogen
- Heat, during all its chemical reactions
- Hormones, such as thrombopoietin (for platelet production in bone marrow), insulin-like growth factor (for cell growth) and angiotensinogen (for controlling blood pressure)
- Proteins that are involved in helping blood to clot
- Bile, to digest fats in the duodenum

It also stockpiles essential nutrients that ensure the body can survive when food is scarce, including:

- Glucose as glycogen
- Various vitamins, including A, B12, D, E and K
- Minerals, such as iron and copper, that are essential for the immune system

GALLBLADDER AND BILE DUCTS

Your gallbladder and bile ducts are also part of your hepatobiliary system, along with your liver. Nestled beneath your liver is your gallbladder, which owes its green hue to its contents: bile. Like your urinary bladder, it is a muscular storage sac. It is connected to your liver via bile ducts, which also form connections with your pancreas and duodenum.

HEPATOBILIARY ISSUES

When something goes amiss with your hepatobiliary system, you often know about it. Gallstones are a common disorder that arise when cholesterol in bile hardens and forms stones in your gallbladder. These can vary in size, shape and number, but they cause major problems if they block the common bile duct through which the pancreas also sends its digestive enzymes to the duodenum. This can result in an inflamed pancreas (pancreatitis), which can be very serious. Symptoms that indicate a problem with your liver or that bile has failed to reach the intestine include pale faeces and yellowing of the whites of the eyes and skin, known as jaundice, caused by the build-up of the pigment bilirubin in your blood.

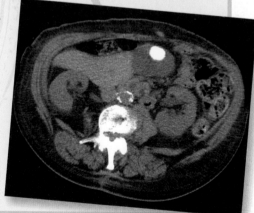

▶ This axial CT image shows a large circular gallstone in the gallbladder. This stone is made of calcium and cholesterol. Dense calcium is typically picked up on CT scans.

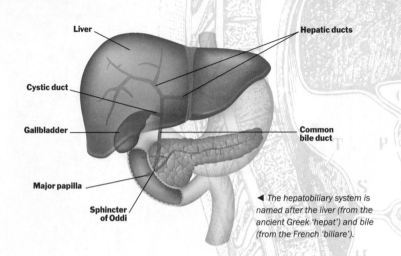

Liver

Hepatic ducts

Cystic duct

Gallbladder

Common bile duct

Major papilla

Sphincter of Oddi

◄ *The hepatobiliary system is named after the liver (from the ancient Greek 'hepat') and bile (from the French 'biliare').*

BILE

Fats are notoriously hard to digest, so your body needs all the help it can get to break down these compounds. Bile has the right ingredients. These include bile salts (e.g. sodium glycocholate and sodium taurocholate), which emulsify fats into smaller droplets so that the lipases have a better chance of breaking them down. Bile's other components include minerals that help neutralize the chyme, cholesterol, and bile pigments that give bile its unique yellow-green colour. These pigments arise from the breakdown of the haeme component of red blood cells into biliverdin, which later transforms into yellow-brown bilirubin that colours and deodorizes your faeces. Bacteria in the intestine break down the bilirubin into urobilin, or urochrome, which is absorbed into the blood and gives urine its straw colour.

GALLBLADDER TO DUODENUM

As soon as food enters the duodenum, especially fatty foods, your duodenum secretes a peptide hormone called cholecystokinin (CCK), which is absorbed into the bloodstream. Upon reaching the gallbladder, CCK causes it to contract and squeeze out bile into the cystic duct. The bile travels along the common bile duct and enters the duodenum via the sphincter of Oddi. The more concentrated the bile, the better it is at breaking down fats.

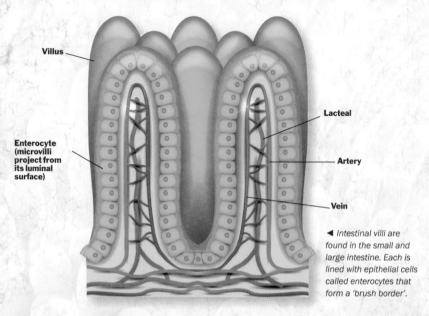

Villus

Lacteal

Enterocyte
(microvilli
project from
its luminal
surface)

Artery

Vein

◄ *Intestinal villi are
found in the small and
large intestine. Each is
lined with epithelial cells
called enterocytes that
form a 'brush border'.*

ABSORPTION TIME

With the chyme neutralized and
digested, the next phase begins. The
lower regions of your GIT contain parts
of the small intestine – the jejunum and
ileum – and all of the large intestine.
This is absorption territory, as your gut
seeks to extract every nutrient and
useful substance it possibly can from
the remnants of the food held captive
within its cavity. In these areas, the
GIT is long, very long.

JEJUNUM

Your jejunum is about 2.5m (8ft) long
and nearly 4cm (1½in) wide. It arises
immediately after the duodenum and
is held in place by the mesentery to the
back of the abdominal wall. Its mucosal
layer is arranged in such a way that it
increases the surface area for absorption.
It does this by utilizing circular folds
that are blanketed with microscopic
1mm (¹⁄₂₅in) long fingerlike projections

called villi. It is here where the rich blood supply that runs in and out of the mesentery ensures that food waste and water are the only things left.

The venules and veins from the intestine converge at the hepatic portal vein that drains into the liver for it to process and store some of the nutrient-rich blood prior to distribution through the body. Each villus contains lymphatic capillaries called lacteals that absorb digested fatty substances (so the blood vessels do not have to) and carry them to the thoracic duct (the largest lymphatic vessel), where they go into the bloodstream. The jejunum gradually morphs into its thinner-walled and narrower counterpart, the ileum.

ILEUM

As the last part of the small intestine, the ileum connects to the large intestine. Held in place by the mesentery, the ileum has the same basic structure as the jejunum but is much longer, around 3.5m (11½ft), accounting for more than half the length of the small intestine.

So what does the ileum do differently from the jejunum? It absorbs water-soluble vitamins, especially vitamin B12 (which is important to your nervous system and helps in production of red blood cells and DNA synthesis). The bile salts sodium glycocholate and sodium taurocholate are also reabsorbed and get recycled in the liver. Finally, the ileum provides another chance for your GIT to absorb whatever products of digestion were missed by the jejunum.

▼ Microvilli are microscopic protrusions of the plasma membrane of cells lining a villus. They help to increase further the surface area available for absorption. Microfilaments can be seen projecting from the cytoplasm.

END OF THE LINE

By the time the food you ate some 12 to 29 hours ago reaches your large intestine, it has changed so much in appearance and composition that it is now designated as waste. Stripped of most of its nutritional value, it must now be forcibly pushed out of your body like an unwanted guest at a nightclub.

LARGE INTESTINE

The large intestine's 1.5m (5ft) length is divided among several key structures, from the caecum to the anus, that help extract water, sodium, potassium, chloride, minerals and vitamins for absorption into the blood as well as compact and store faeces ready for expulsion. The lining of the large intestine is punctuated with crypts,

Transverse colon: Crosses the abdomen from left to right

Ascending colon: Waste moves upward via peristalsis.

Caecum: Collects waste from the small intestine

Appendix: A vestigial organ, a remnant of an organ involved in digesting foliage used by our ancestors long ago. It is also believed to be a possible safe house for gut bacteria.

Large intestine

Descending colon: On the left side of your abdomen

Sigmoid colon: Forms an S-shaped loop. Faeces continues to be compacted and is kept moist by the mucus secretions of goblet cells.

Anus: Faeces are expelled along with the gaseous byproducts of waste fermentation by gut microbes, such as methane and hydrogen sulphide, producing those characteristic sounds and smells.

Rectum: Faeces are temporarily stored here before being expelled through the anus. As the amount of faeces increases, this activates stretch receptors that trigger a reflex arc. The internal anal sphincter relaxes and higher cerebral input makes it possible to feel the need to defecate and make the decision to relax the external anal sphincter.

which are glands that absorb water, and cells that secrete mucus to aid the transit of waste.

It can take many hours, more than a day (with it taking longer, on average, for women than men), for waste to transit through the large intestine, but the time is reduced if fibre is present.

GUT BACTERIA

Most of food's nutritional value has been absorbed by the time the large intestine is reached, but not all. Your GIT has a final act waiting in the bowels of your intestine – your gut bacteria or microbiome. This diverse community of trillions of microbes that line your lower GIT have formed a symbiotic relationship with you and are as specific to you as your fingertips. They also change on a daily basis depending on your diet and lifestyle. Gut bacteria digest those substances you are unable to break down, such as starches, complex sugars and fibres, to generate energy for themselves. In doing so, they help release further nutrients that are absorbed into your blood. In addition, they release substances that kill harmful bacteria, secrete essential vitamins

▲ A computer illustration shows the friendly gut microbe Bifidobacterium. These bacteria are predominately found in your gut as well as your mouth and the vagina.

such as vitamin K, and facilitate the absorption of minerals into your body by fermenting cellulose fibres. They also break down bilirubin, which gives faeces its characteristic brown colour.

Significant changes to the balance of bacteria in your gut could damage your health. Scientists are finding out that gut imbalance is linked to obesity, depression, heart disease and high blood pressure. It is important the balance is kept in check, in particular by avoiding those substances that kill them, including antibiotics and alcohol.

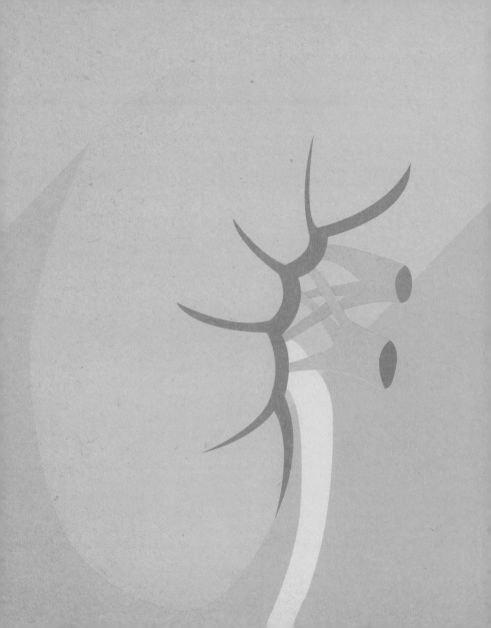

CHAPTER 11

YOUR WASTE PLUMBING SYSTEM

THE URINARY SYSTEM

Peeing, urination, weeing or micturition… all these terms describe the end-process of the urinary system. You are usually only aware that you have this system because of the sensation and need to void its main product, urine, from your bladder – an organ that not only stores urine but also regularly beckons you to start proceedings when it is full. The organs and structures that make up your urinary system work quietly like back-of-house staff, continuously producing that straw-coloured concoction as they strive to keep you chemically balanced and free of the things you do not need.

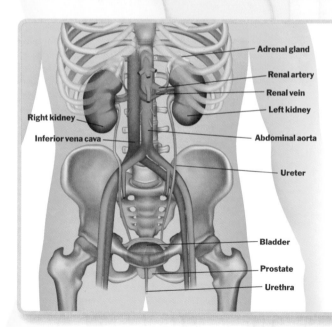

Adrenal gland

Renal artery

Renal vein

Left kidney

Right kidney

Inferior vena cava

Abdominal aorta

Ureter

Bladder

Prostate

Urethra

URINARY SYSTEM

◄ Your kidneys and bladder, protected respectively by your lower ribcage and pelvic bone, form the main organs of your urinary system. Your ureters and urethra aid the passage of urine from your kidneys and bladder.

ALL IN A NAME

Your urinary system is sometimes referred to as your renal system or urinary tract. It is also part of your excretory system, which includes the digestive system and organs such as your skin, lungs and liver. Collectively, these organs help rid your body of metabolic waste like carbon dioxide, electrolytes, excess water, undigested food and harmful products and toxins via a pungent mix of urine, sweat, faecal matter and exhaled breath.

Sometimes your urinary system is grouped together with your genitals and referred to as your urogenital or genitourinary system. This is largely because they recruit common structures to function and are also embryonically related, which means they share similar nerve pathways and tracts.

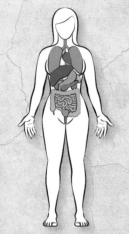

▲ Your excretory system recruits your skin and various internal organs to rid you of unwanted substances.

High up there in the urinary pecking order are those bean-shaped organs called kidneys. These smooth-skinned paired filtration hubs, located either side of your mid-spine, are the structures that produce urine. Kidneys also have their own uniquely arranged blood supply to help them filter your plasma and are equipped with plumbing fixtures and pipes that collect the filtrate and lead into tubes that descend toward your main storage tank, which is the bladder.

Under your direct control, the urine is then released through internal valves along more pipework before it jets or trickles out into the external environment. Since the lower urinary system has to deal with fluid that varies in volume, it is important that the cells that make up its various structures and organs are flexible enough to extend and retract when necessary. That is why they have a unique covering called the urothelium, a type of flattened epithelium that can expand and recoil.

THE TWO KIDNEYS

To describe the main functions of your kidneys is to explain the entire purpose of the urinary system, for its remaining organs and structures serve as mere piping and storage for the kidneys' end product: urine.

Renal cortex: Contains blood vessels and little filtration-cum-absorption units called nephrons. Cortical nephrons are found here, including the upper parts of nephrons found in the medulla, called juxtamedullary nephrons.

Renal medulla: Contains the renal pyramids and extensions of the cortex that divide the medulla into pyramids.

Renal pyramid: Contains most of the tubular parts of the nephrons that transport the urine produced in the cortical regions toward the calyx and ultimately the ureter (see pages 262–3).

Renal artery: This offshoot of the abdominal aorta transports blood to the kidneys. It splits into arcuate arteries that give rise to afferent arterioles and subsequent glomeruli (capillaries) and efferent arterioles (see page 262).

Renal vein: Drains the kidney and merges with the inferior cava.

Renal pelvis: A wide funnel and first part of the ureter that urine drains into.

Renal capsule

Major calyx: Two or three minor calyces converge to form a major calyx.

Minor calyx: Minor calyces are chambers at the top of the pyramids, through which urine passes.

▲ Cut a kidney in half in a coronal plane and you will see that it contains several different structures.

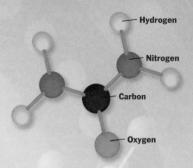

- Hydrogen
- Nitrogen
- Carbon
- Oxygen

◀ *This is the molecular structure of urea, a nitrogenous waste product of protein metabolism.*

Your kidneys are part shielded by your lowest ribs. The right kidney is slightly smaller and sits lower, because your liver rests above it. Each kidney is coated with a thin renal capsule made of fibrous connective tissue. You can live with just one healthy kidney, although not without risks: the extra one is a reserve in case the other malfunctions or is damaged.

WORK OF THE KIDNEYS

The kidneys' main role is to filter your blood to ensure the amounts of water and salts in your body fluids are constant. This is vital because imbalance in the levels of ions such as potassium, sodium and calcium can have dire consequences for your nervous and muscular systems. Similarly, your kidneys ensure your body fluids are the correct pH. If they are too acidic, you risk developing the condition acidosis, which can be life threatening; too alkaline and you could develop alkalosis, which can lead to muscular and nervous impairments. Your kidneys, therefore, excrete as necessary those ions that dictate acidity and alkalinity, such as hydrogen ions and bicarbonate.

As part of your excretory system, your kidneys also get rid of any toxic and metabolic waste products, such as urea (see page 249) and creatinine (a breakdown product from muscles). Other tasks performed by your kidneys are summarized on page 267.

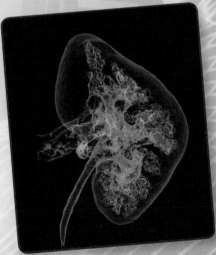

▶ *This CT scan shows the cortex, medulla, calyces and renal hilium, the central part of the kidney where the vessels, nerves and ureter enter/exit.*

NEPHRONS

Each kidney contains over a million tiny structures called nephrons. They are made up of two parts: a renal corpuscle and renal tubule. Depending on their location, nephrons are categorized as cortical or juxtamedullary.

RENAL CORPUSCLES

Filtration happens in spherical structures called renal corpuscles. These contain a capillary network called glomeruli, which emerge from afferent arterioles and wind into a cup-like structure called a Bowman's capsule. This creates enormous pressure, which forces the water and waste dissolved in the blood to filter out of the capillaries through specialized pores and enter the Bowman's capsule, which is the initial part of the nephron's tubule.

GLOMERULI

These knots of capillaries form the first of two capillary beds in the nephron. The glomeruli create a surface area of over 500cm² (78in²) for filtration. Their capillary walls form a sieve that

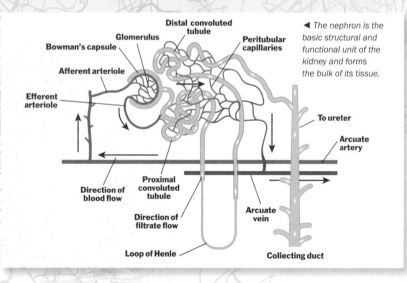

Distal convoluted tubule

Glomerulus

Bowman's capsule

Peritubular capillaries

Afferent arteriole

Efferent arteriole

To ureter

Arcuate artery

Direction of blood flow

Proximal convoluted tubule

Direction of filtrate flow

Arcuate vein

Loop of Henle

Collecting duct

◀ *The nephron is the basic structural and functional unit of the kidney and forms the bulk of its tissue.*

allows small molecules, such as water, salts, hormones, glucose and water-soluble vitamins, to filter out and into the Bowman's capsule. Large molecules, such as blood cells and plasma proteins like albumin, cannot pass. The filtered blood leaves the glomeruli via the efferent arteriole, which branches into the second capillary bed, the peritubular capillaries and vasa recta tangling round the loop of Henle, before it enters the venous system.

RENAL TUBULES

The Bowman's capsule narrows to form the proximal convoluted tubule. This is surrounded by the peritubular capillaries and vasa recta, which reabsorb water, nutrients and solutes in the filtrate into the blood. To maximize their reabsorption, the epithelial cells lining the tubule have microvilli that increase the surface area. These cells also contain many mitochondria that supply the energy needed to transport these solutes against their concentration gradient.

As the tubule turns downward, it forms the descending limb of the loop of Henle. Here, large amounts of water are reabsorbed into the blood, as the tubule's permeability changes to water only. Next, the ascending limb of the loop connects to the less active distal convoluted tubule, which flows to the collecting ducts.

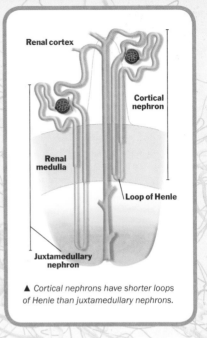

▲ *Cortical nephrons have shorter loops of Henle than juxtamedullary nephrons.*

COLLECTING DUCTS

These ducts are not part of the nephron: they collect filtrate from several nephrons and finalize the concentration of urine. This is regulated by the pituitary hormone anti-diuretic hormone (ADH), which increases their permeability to water, allowing more to be reabsorbed into the blood. This explains why your urine is more concentrated in the morning, because you release more ADH at night. The filtrate (now urine) passes from the collecting ducts into the emerging calyces, renal pelvis and ureter.

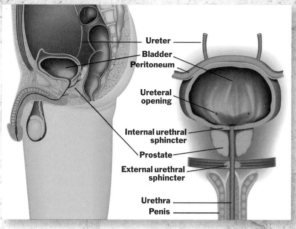

Ureter —
Bladder
Peritoneum
Ureteral opening
Internal urethral sphincter
Prostate
External urethral sphincter
Urethra
Penis

After leaving the kidneys, urine passes through the accessory organs of the urinary system: the two ureters, the bladder and urethra. The last of these is different lengths in men and women.

◀ *The male urinary system*

ACCESSORY ORGANS

URETER

These thin muscular tubes, about 30cm (12in) long, run from the renal hilium of each kidney to the back of the bladder. Just as food passes down the oesophagus in waves via peristalsis, the ureters help gravity draw urine toward the bladder by periodically constricting and relaxing the smooth muscle in their walls. The ureters enter the bladder obliquely, or slanted, which helps to prevent backflow of urine. In addition, vesicoureteral valves at the junction of bladder and ureter ensure the flow is one way when the bladder is full.

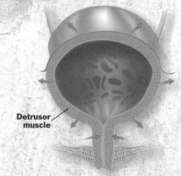

Detrusor muscle

▲ *As your bladder fills, the detrusor muscle relaxes and the internal urethral sphincter contracts.*

BLADDER

This hollow organ with a thick muscular wall sits in the pelvic basin between your rectum and pubic bone, with the small intestine (plus the womb in females) on top. Inside the bladder are folds called rugae, which stretch and smooth out as it fills with urine. You have the capacity to hold anywhere between 400 and 600ml (13.5 and 20fl oz) of urine before pain receptors and stretch receptors are activated, letting you know it is time to go.

The bladder utilizes the voluntary and involuntary parts of your nervous system to regulate its activities in a highly coordinated fashion. The autonomic nervous system controls the detrusor muscle in the bladder wall and an internal ring of tissue called the internal urethral sphincter. As urine begins to accumulate, sympathetic nerves of the autonomic nervous system cause the internal sphincter to close, and prevent the detrusor muscles from contracting. Stretch receptors in the muscle walls signal it is time to urinate. Parasympathetic nerves stimulate the muscle layer to contract, to aid emptying, and the internal sphincter to relax. However, nothing leaves without your say so, as the motor nerves of the somatic nervous system control the external sphincter. You learn how to constrict this muscle during potty training.

URETHRA

This exit hose of the urinary system leaves the bladder at its lowest point to avoid urine stagnation. In women, the urethra is about 4cm (1½in) and found between the clitoris and vagina. It has only one function: to release urine. In men, however, the urethra is about 20cm (8in) long. It passes through the prostate gland, which sits underneath the bladder, and subsequently hijacks the penis as its exit route. Thankfully, ejaculation and urination cannot happen at the same time. Because of the close relationship between the prostate and urinary system in men, frequent urination or a weak stream is often an early sign of an enlarged prostate. In more severe cases, when the urethral opening is completely obscured, this becomes a medical emergency as it can lead to urinary tract and kidney problems.

◀ An enlarged prostate can block the passage of urine through the urethra and heighten the sensation of needing to pee.

PEE

Pee, wee, a number one – these are just some of the monikers used to describe that blood-derived biofluid called urine. At 95 per cent water, urine contains small hydrophilic molecules that are either innocuous substances that you no longer need or cannot store, or are harmful compounds that must be eliminated. Urine is naturally sterile and gets its yellow colour from bacteria in your intestine (see page 251).

You produce about 0.8 to 2l (28 to 70fl oz) of urine every day, depending on your level of hydration. Factors such as how much water you drink, diet, activity levels and the temperature of your external environment, determine its volume, constituents, smell and colour. Straw-coloured urine signals a healthy urinary system, while dark amber signifies too little water or a potential problem. Urine has a faint odour that can

DRINK YOUR OWN?

Some people revere urine as a health-sustaining drink and skin tonic. However, there is currently no peer-reviewed medical evidence to suggest that urophagia, the practice of drinking your own urine, benefits your health. The contents of that 5 per cent of urine that is not water should be borne in mind, as it contains the nitrogenous waste products of metabolism, such as urea, uric acid and creatinine. High levels of these products could lead to the medical condition azotemia. Furthermore, although excess salts, hormones and water-soluble vitamins may seem innocuous, your body eliminates these to prevent them building up and disrupting critical processes.

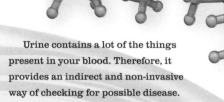

The kidney produces the active form of vitamin D, calcitriol.

smell like ammonia if concentrated or allowed to stand. Various food pigments, such as beetroot, can colour it, while foods such as asparagus bequeath it a distinct odour, although not everyone can produce or detect it.

Urine contains a lot of the things present in your blood. Therefore, it provides an indirect and non-invasive way of checking for possible disease.

A VERY USEFUL SYSTEM

In addition to filtering your blood, your urinary system has other functions:

Vitamin D activation: The kidneys are the third-line reserve for converting vitamin D from its inactive to its active form (calcitriol). This travels to the small intestine, where it facilitates formation of proteins capable of binding to calcium.

Red blood cell production: The kidneys double up as endocrine glands, secreting the hormone erythropoietin, which stimulates stem cells in the bone marrow to produce more erythrocytes. Kidney fibroblast cells are sensitive to low oxygen levels in the blood that passes through the kidneys.

Blood pressure regulation: When blood pressure is low, the kidneys produce a peptide hormone enzyme called renin (aka angiotensinogenase), which is a key component of the renin-angiotensin hormone system that involves the cleavage of lots of proteins and the activation of pro-enzymes. When renin is released into the blood, it binds to the protein angiotensinogen (produced by the liver) and cleaves it to form angiotensin I. In the lungs, angiotensin I is cleaved by an enzyme called angiotensin-converting enzyme (ACE) into angiotensin II, which causes the smooth muscle of the arteriole walls to constrict and increase blood pressure. If levels of sodium are low, angiotensin II triggers the adrenal glands to secrete the hormone aldosterone, which instructs the kidneys' distal tubules and collecting ducts to reabsorb more sodium ions in exchange for potassium ions. This causes water to also be reabsorbed, which increases blood volume and pressure.

Calcium reabsorption: Parathyroid hormones stimulate the kidney tubules to reabsorb more calcium when blood levels get low.

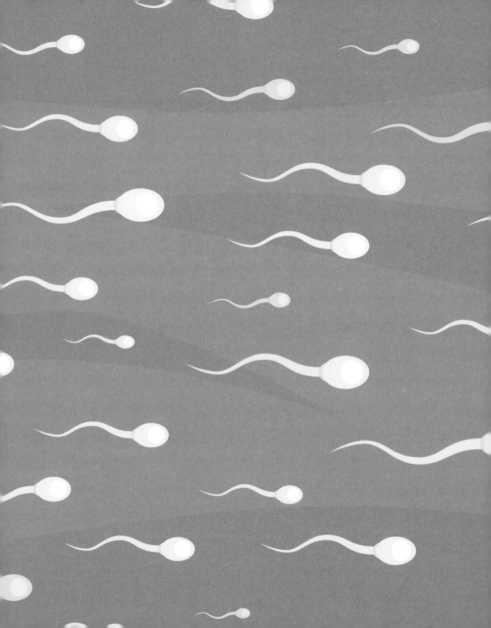

CHAPTER 12

BABY-MAKING TOOLS

THE REPRODUCTIVE SYSTEM

Your reproductive system is the second of your organ systems associated with pleasure. (The first was the digestive system.) From an evolutionary perspective, this must mean that it has an important function not just for your own existence but for the very survival of the species. Consequently, it should come as no surprise to learn that linking the most important of functions (on a population level) with the most pleasurable of activities (on an individual level) ensures that reproduction is never too far away.

MALE REPRODUCTIVE SYSTEM

FEMALE REPRODUCTIVE SYSTEM

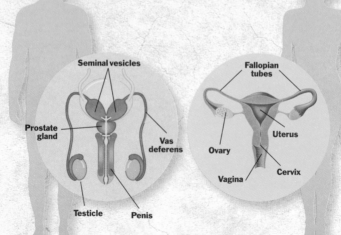

Seminal vesicles

Prostate gland

Vas deferens

Testicle

Penis

Fallopian tubes

Uterus

Ovary

Cervix

Vagina

	MALE	**FEMALE**	
Gonads	Testes (2)	Ovaries (2)	
External genitals	Penis	Vulva	Clitoris
	Scrotum		Labia (lips)
		Hymen	
Internal genitals	Prostate	Vagina	
	Seminal vesicles (2)	Cervix	
	Epididymis and ductus (vas) deferens (tubes of the genital tract)	Uterus	
		Fallopian tubes (2)	

You are equipped with the apparatus to reproduce whether you plan to or not. These baby-making tools determine what sex you belong to and the role you play in bringing new life into the world. However, it is not as simple as that. Gender identity, sexual preference and fertility problems all exemplify the complexity of the sensitive and extremely important issues that swirl around gender and reproduction. Those matters aside, your sexual apparatus, from an evolutionary point of view, is geared toward one goal – getting an egg to meet a sperm.

This event first becomes a possibility after puberty, when a child turns into an adult and their gonads and genitals mature. Your gonads are sometimes referred to as your primary sex organs. They are the first to be stimulated during puberty by gonadotropic hormones released by the pituitary gland.

Once activated, the gonads themselves release hormones that drive the maturation of genitalia and the development of secondary sexual characteristics that make us either male or female.

THE BIG CHANGE

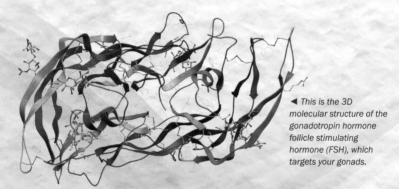

◄ This is the 3D molecular structure of the gonadotropin hormone follicle stimulating hormone (FSH), which targets your gonads.

Your body transitions from child to adult on the back of a momentous physiological event called puberty. Controlled by hormones, puberty induces emotional and physical changes that last a lifetime. It represents the end of childhood and the beginning of an adventure full of trials and tribulations as well as, hopefully, pleasure and fulfilment.

PUBERTY TRIGGERS

For centuries, the exact trigger for puberty remained a mystery. Today, research suggests that weight and levels of body fat could be linked to the onset of puberty. This revolves around the theory that your body waits until it has reached a certain baseline weight that ensures there are enough resources before it commits to the big change. In boys, a higher weight threshold is required, which is why puberty usually starts slightly later. It is believed that once the hormone leptin released from body fat (see page 233) reaches a certain level, the hypothalamus

is triggered to activate the pituitary gland and sends pulses of gonadotropin releasing hormone. This initiates the release of luteinizing hormone (LH) and follicle stimulating hormone (FSH) into the bloodstream, which have either your testes or ovaries as their prime target.

GROWTH SPURT

Puberty initiates a rapid growth spurt orchestrated by the release of growth hormones from the anterior pituitary gland. Growth hormone (GH) stimulates

▲ Both boys and girls produce oestrogen, which triggers the release of growth hormone (GH) from the pituitary gland.

▼ The journey from baby to old age is punctuated with changes, the most formidable during puberty.

your liver to produce a hormone called insulin-like growth factor 1 (IGF-1). This triggers growth of muscle and cartilage found in the epiphysial plate of your long bones. During puberty, things are ramped up with the help of oestrogen, produced by both sexes but in greater amounts in girls, which causes the brain to release IGF-1. This may explain why girls grow faster than boys during puberty.

Cartilage cells in the epiphysial plate undergo rapid division, pushing older cells toward the centre. These squash and harden, gradually elongating the long bones by as much as 7 to 10cm (3–4in) in a year. With suddenly larger limbs, your brain has to readjust as your centre of balance changes. This helps to explain the clumsy nature of the teen.

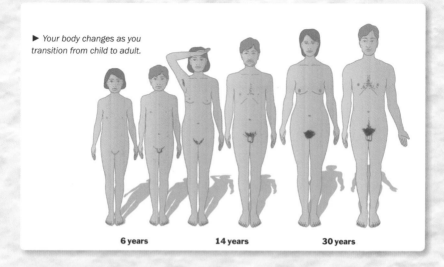

▶ Your body changes as you transition from child to adult.

6 years   **14 years**   **30 years**

BODY CHANGES

Most of the changes that arise during puberty are dependent on your sex. However, some are common to both, including the growth of hair in your armpits and pubic regions, and acne arising from the hormonal stimulation of your sebaceous glands, which oversecrete sebum and take a while to balance the amount of oil they release.

MALE PUBERTY

Although the onset of puberty varies between individuals, most boys enter puberty at 9–12 years old and complete most of it around their 18th birthday. When stimulated by LH, testes release testosterone and other androgens into the bloodstream, which floods the body with these man-making substances. FSH initiates the production of sperm. Boys also produce oestrogen, when testosterone is converted by the enzyme aromatase to oestrogenic compounds.

FEMALE PUBERTY

For girls, puberty usually starts between 8 and 11 years, although it can be earlier or later. It is usually completed by the age of 15 to 19. When stimulated by LH and FSH, the ovaries begin to produce progesterone, including testosterone, which is converted to oestrogen (known as oestradiol in humans). Oestrogen floods the body and initiates the changes associated with sexual maturity.

BOY-SPECIFIC CHANGES

Body hair	Thicker body hair grows on the face, abdomen, arms and legs.
Testes	Testes mature and grow larger. Sperm production begins and the first ejaculate of semen, known as a 'wet dream', occurs at night.
Muscular	Muscles grow larger.
Bone changes	The ribs, shoulders, long bones, jaw, brow or supraorbital ridge grow larger, as do the voice box and larynx, which also gain thicker and longer vocal cords.
Genitalia	The external genitals grow larger and thicker.

GIRL-SPECIFIC CHANGES

Breast growth	Tender breast buds appear as the nipples become more pronounced and the breast tissue and fat develops. However, full development of breast tissue is not complete until a woman has her first child.
Uterus	The uterus, or womb, grows larger, to about the size of a clenched fist. The inner lining, called the endometrium, becomes more vascularized. The fallopian tubes also mature. The first menstrual bleeding, known as menarche, occurs on average around the age of 12, a couple of years after the secondary sexual characteristics first appear. Preliminary periods tend to be irregular and anovulatory (arising without the release of an egg) for about the first year.
Ovaries	These secrete oestrogen and progesterone and, following a surge of LH, begin the process of ovulation.
Vagina	One of the first signs of puberty is a creamy white discharge from the vagina. This is due to changing hormone levels and usually indicates that a period will arrive within a year or so. The vagina also grows larger and lengthens, with its walls becoming thicker.
Genitalia	The vulva and clitoris enlarge.
Body fat	There is increased body fat deposition on the hips, buttocks, stomach and thighs.
Pelvic girdle	This begins to widen in preparation for carrying a child.

A GENTLEMAN'S ANATOMY

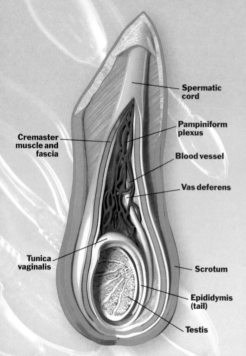

Spermatic cord

Pampiniform plexus

Blood vessel

Vas deferens

Cremaster muscle and fascia

Tunica vaginalis

Scrotum

Epididymis (tail)

Testis

▲ *The scrotum sits outside the abdominal cavity to keep the temperature of the testes a little lower.*

It appears that the whole purpose of the male reproductive system is to produce sperm and deposit it in the female. This sounds quite simple, which – you might say – probably explains a lot.

TESTES

During fetal development, testes start in the abdomen and gradually move to their resting place in the scrotum. Each is about the size of a quail's egg and is where sperm is made and testosterone released into the blood. It contains seminiferous tubules whose walls provide the site of sperm production, also known as spermatogenesis. Billions are produced every month by meiosis (see page 39) and spermiogenesis – the final maturation stage. Each sperm cell ends up with one half the total number of chromosomes needed: 23. This is because the full number of chromosomes, 46, is restored when it fertilizes an egg, which also has 23 chromosomes.

Developing sperm cells are nourished by nearby Sertoli cells, while Leydig cells produce the hormone testosterone. Immature sperm cells (spermatids) migrate into the central area, or lumen, of the seminiferous tubules. These young sperm cells are immobile, so leave the testes only when the tubules contract and squeeze them out toward the epididymis. The epididymis is made of tiny tubes, folded many times, that if stretched out would be 6 to 7m (20 to 23ft) long. The immature sperm are stored in the epididymis as they mature.

The epididymis connects with the vas deferens, which travels behind the bladder and joins the seminal duct to form the ejaculatory duct (see page 278). The vas deferens is what is cut during a vasectomy. Once ejaculation occurs, it can take up to two days for the epididymis to refill.

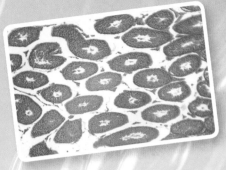

▲ A histological section through a testicle shows many seminiferous tubules (pink).

A SPERM CELL

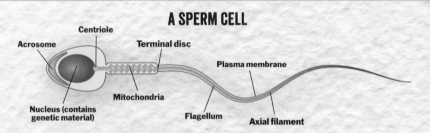

Acrosome
Centriole
Terminal disc
Plasma membrane
Mitochondria
Nucleus (contains genetic material)
Flagellum
Axial filament

The ideal temperature for sperm development in the testes is about 1.7°C (3°F) lower than the rest of the body. The scrotum has muscles that pull the testes closer to the body to warm them if need be. If it gets too hot, the scrotum relaxes its blood vessels to let heat dissipate. A single sperm cell (spermatozoon) is about 0.05mm (0.002in) long. When mature, the front part of a sperm's 'head', or acrosome, contains enzymes that can penetrate the ovum. The midsection is packed with mitochondria to ensure it has energy during its journey to the ovum. In the epididymis, there are about 300 million sperm per ml. Not all are perfectly formed, even among men with no fertility problems: some spermatozoa have two heads, a large or misshapen head, or two tails. Spermatozoa with two heads are unlikely to penetrate the ovum, while those with other abnormalities may result in failed pregnancies. Spermatozoa that are not ejaculated will disintegrate and be reabsorbed. A lot are also lost in urine.

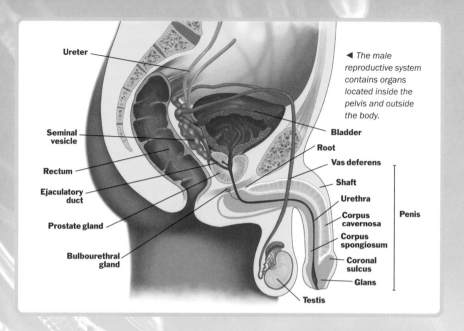

The male reproductive system contains organs located inside the pelvis and outside the body.

Labels (clockwise):
Ureter
Bladder
Root
Vas deferens
Shaft
Urethra
Corpus cavernosa
Corpus spongiosum
Coronal sulcus
Glans
Penis
Testis
Bulbourethral gland
Prostate gland
Ejaculatory duct
Rectum
Seminal vesicle

SEMEN

During ejaculation, sperm passes through the ejaculatory ducts and mixes with fluids from the seminal vesicles, prostate gland and bulbourethral glands (also known as Cowper's glands) to form semen. These glands all secrete alkaline fluid that helps to raise the pH of semen to counteract the acidic environment of the female reproductive tract. This also helps to activate the sperms' tails and increase their motility.

Seminal vesicles: This pair of glands produce most of the fluid that makes up semen. They make a yellowish fluid that aids transport of sperm and contains sugars like fructose to help nourish sperm. The seminal vesicles also produce substances called prostaglandins that facilitate the movement of sperm up the female tract. Their ducts converge with the vas deferens to form the ejaculatory duct that passes through the prostate gland and empties into the urethra.

Prostate gland: At the base of the bladder, this gland surrounds the urethra and contracts during an ejaculation to add its own milky white secretion to the seminal fluid. It helps ensure that the semen liquifies to aid passage of sperm.

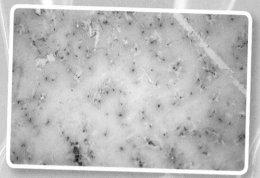

◄ In this image of semen under a microscope, the heads and tails of the spermatozoa are clearly visible.

Bulbourethral glands: These two glands are about the size of a pea and secrete a clear alkaline fluid primarily to neutralize any acidic remnant of urine in the urethra that could damage the sperm.

PENIS

It is the structure that most people focus on when it comes to the male sex organs and its size can be a source of confidence or despair. Its job is to deposit sperm deep inside the vagina (as well as being an exit point for urine). The penis also provides men with considerable pleasure with and without a sexual partner. For many men, waking up with a fully erect penis is usually a sign that their erectile tissue is in good working order. This 'morning glory' is the last stage of a series of night-time erections that are believed to occur during rapid eye movement when dreaming. The penis has several key parts:

Urethra: Running through the centre of the penis, this is for urine and semen exit. It is connected to your bladder, with a tight ring of muscle to prevent urine from flowing. The seminal vesicle ducts and vas deferens join the urethra near where it leaves the bladder.

Glans: This is the most sensitive part of the penis, particularly around the rim (coronal sulcus).

Shaft: The main body contains spongy tissue called the corpus cavernosa and corpus spongiosum. These become engorged with blood when the penis is erect. The shaft's length varies depending on whether it is flaccid or erect and also differs between individuals. When the penis is flaccid, it has a root-to-tip length of 6–12cm ($2^3/_8$–$4^3/_4$in). An erect penis can be 10–20cm (4–8in) long.

Root: The base of the penis attaches to the groin.

Foreskin: This fold of skin protects the glans during non-sexual activity. It is sometimes removed (during circumcision). When the penis is erect, it peels back. It also produces a lubricant called smegma which, if not washed regularly, can form a cheesy build-up and cause inflammation.

A LADY'S ANATOMY

'Man may work from sun to sun, but woman's work is never done,' goes the old English saying. This analysis of job share can be extended to the process of reproduction, where it is clear that a woman's job is considerably larger. Not only does a woman produce the eggs that get fertilized, but she also has the responsibility to nourish the new life growing inside her. In preparation for this mammoth task, girls' bodies tend to transition into puberty much earlier than boys'.

OVARIES

These oval-shaped structures, which lie either side of the uterus, are held in place by strong elasticated ligaments. Ovaries are just over 3cm (1⅛in) long and 1cm (⅖in) thick. They provide a site for eggs, or ova, to mature prior to their release during ovulation.

Ovaries house around a million or so eggs at birth, all the eggs a woman will need in her lifetime. Production of ova occurs via a process called oogenesis and involves the meiotic division of germ cells (see page 39), resulting in each ovum containing half the total number of chromosomes. The full completion of the second

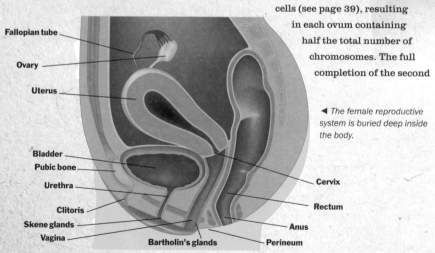

◀ The female reproductive system is buried deep inside the body.

Fallopian tube
Ovary
Uterus
Bladder
Pubic bone
Urethra
Clitoris
Skene glands
Vagina
Bartholin's glands
Cervix
Rectum
Anus
Perineum

meiotic division occurs at the point of fertilization. Because oogenesis occurs in a female fetus prior to birth, a mother carrying a daughter is also supporting the eggs that make her grandchildren. The number of eggs that a woman carries in her ovaries dwindles over her lifetime. By the time she reaches puberty, only around 500,000 ova are left.

Ovaries also serve as endocrine organs. They release the female sex hormones progesterone and oestrogen, which work together to maintain the growth of the uterine wall in preparation for a potential pregnancy. The ovaries also secrete small amounts of testosterone, which helps fuel sex drive.

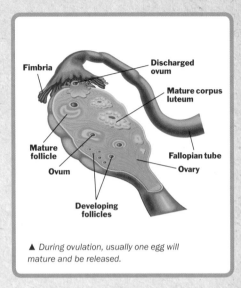

▲ During ovulation, usually one egg will mature and be released.

FEMALE EXTERNAL GENITALIA

Clitoris	This is the female equivalent of the penis. Extremely sensitive, it serves as the organ of sexual excitement. Similarly to a penis, its spongy tissue fills with blood when aroused.
Labia	These 'lips' or skin folds are developmentally equivalent to the male scrotum. The labia majora are the outermost folds, while the labia minora are the innermost lesser lips, which cover the clitoris like a protective hood. The labia minora also contain erectile tissue and become enlarged during sex.
Hymen	It has no known functional significance, although culturally it has served as an indicator of a female's virginity and is named after the Greek god of marriage, Hymenaios. This mucosal thin sheath of tissue that covers or partially covers the entrance to the vagina comes in many variations and can be perforated with one or several holes or none at all. It can easily be torn by use of a tampon or by strenuous exercise.
Glands	When a woman gets sexually aroused, the entrance to the vagina is lubricated by the secretions of the pea-sized Bartholin's glands. Near the opening of the urethra are Skene glands, which secrete alkaline fluid to counteract the acidic nature of vaginal fluids.

VAGINA

If the penis is the main focus among male sexual organs, the female equivalent should rightly be the clitoris. But often in pop culture the vagina takes prominence because sex has historically been viewed from the male perspective of prioritizing penile fulfilment via vaginal stimulation. That being said, the front wall of the vagina is believed to be where a woman's erogenous zone resides. Known as the G-spot, or Grafenberg spot, its existence is not universally agreed by scientists – and is subjective from woman to woman.

The vagina serves as a channel to the uterus. To accommodate the penis, its size is usually about two-thirds the length of a penis. Its muscular and fibrous walls are lined with flat squamous epithelial cells in a corrugated fashion that facilitates vaginal expansion during intercourse and also during childbirth.

UTERUS

The uterus, also called the womb, is the shape of an inverted small pear. The top part is called the corpus, or body of the uterus, and the lower part is its neck, or cervix. The uterus is found in the pelvic region, almost big-spooning the bladder, and is held in place by bands of connective tissue and ligaments and supported by pelvic floor muscles. The uterus is mostly hollow unless it is carrying a baby, when it expands to many times its original size to accommodate the fetus. The uterus has an inner layer called the endometrium and a muscle layer called the myometrium. Fibroids are oestrogen-triggered growths composed of muscle and fibrous tissue that can grow anywhere within or outside the uterine wall. Although harmless and often

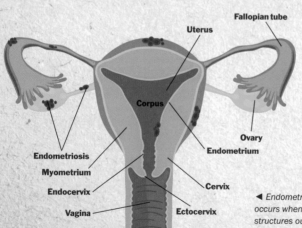

◀ Endometriosis is a painful disease that occurs when endometrial tissue appears on structures outside the womb.

symptomless, they can become extremely painful and debilitating and, at worst, affect a woman's ability to get pregnant or go full term during pregnancy.

CERVIX

The neck of the uterus is about 2.5cm (1in) long. Its lower part, the ectocervix, projects into the vagina and has a small opening that can be felt as a dimple. The ectocervix produces antibodies as another weapon against bacteria, as the fallopian tubes provide a direct route to the abdomen. Glands in the endocervix make mucus that changes during ovulation, in terms of amount, consistency and pH, to facilitate the entry of sperm into the uterus. The cells lining the cervix are often checked via smears, also called Pap tests, for abnormalities. These cells are vulnerable to infection with human papilloma virus, which increases the risk of cervical cancer.

FALLOPIAN TUBES

These emanate from either side of the corpus like long arms with thin, petal-like fingers called fimbria that connect to each ovary. Prior to ovulation, the fimbria swell up and gently sweep the ovary to collect the egg released into the peritoneal cavity, sending it into the fallopian tube.

GOOD AND BAD BACTERIA

The vagina produces acidic secretions that can harm sperm, but this low pH is necessary to impede the growth of harmful bacteria, given that it is an open route into the body situated close to the anus. Since not all bacteria is harmful, a delicate balance of good versus bad bacteria exists in the vagina. If this balance is disturbed by, for example, douching with water or a cleansing agent, this can cause the overgrowth of anaerobic bacteria and yeast that normally exist in the vagina at low levels. This can lead to bacterial vaginosis, an inflammatory condition that produces a strong fishy odour, or the more common yeast infection, which can also arise simply from changes in hormonal levels or from taking certain medications.

▼ *The fungus* Candida albicans *causes thrush.*

THE MENSTRUAL CYCLE

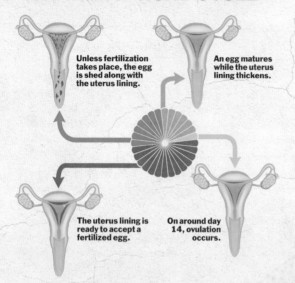

Unless fertilization takes place, the egg is shed along with the uterus lining.

An egg matures while the uterus lining thickens.

The uterus lining is ready to accept a fertilized egg.

On around day 14, ovulation occurs.

Ovulation and menstruation take place about 300 to 400 times in a woman's life. It all starts when follicle stimulating hormone (FSH) triggers the maturation of several sleeping follicles in one of the two ovaries.

◄ *Once a girl reaches puberty, this monthly event continues until she enters the menopause, temporarily stopping during pregnancy and breastfeeding.*

Once a month, a woman's body prepares itself for a possible pregnancy. Over a period of about 28 days, her reproductive organs undergo a series of coordinated changes controlled by hormones released by the pituitary gland. The exact length of time varies according to each individual and their lifestyle and may be longer or shorter in any given month.

AN EGG MATURES

Although the gonadotropic hormones both work together, FSH is chiefly responsible for stimulating the maturation of the egg follicles that lie dormant in the ovaries. An ovarian follicle is a fluid-filled sac that contains an immature egg, or oocyte. Once activated, the follicles start to produce oestrogen to get the lining of the uterus ready for a possible pregnancy. During each cycle, usually only one egg will take centre stage by having a growth spurt and maturing. The remaining egg follicles are reabsorbed by the body. This is the main way in which women lose their eggs: it is estimated that up to 1,000 follicles are lost every month at a rate that increases with age. The cycle stops when the follicles fail to produce enough oestrogen and the woman enters the menopause.

OVULATION

About halfway through the menstrual cycle, the oestrogen levels peak and the pituitary gland releases a sudden burst of LH and FSH. Known as an LH surge, it causes the follicle to rupture and release its egg around 24 hours later. Ovulation test kits measure this surge in LH. The egg then enters the fallopian tube, where its fate is determined.

MENSTRUATION

If fertilization takes place, the monthly cycle halts until the baby is born and the mother stops breastfeeding. If no fertilization occurs, the egg is shed along with the thickened lining of the uterus. Menstrual fluid is a combination of blood and endometrial tissue, which sloughs off over a period of about 5 days, mixed with vaginal secretions and cervical mucus. For those who bleed moderately, total menstrual fluid averages 6 to 8 teaspoons. Substances called prostaglandins released by cells of the endometrium constrict blood

BETTER EDUCATION

It is ironic that the word menstruation starts with 'men', who often feel uncomfortable around the subject and see it as a sensitive girl's issue. The problem is that a lot of women see it as just that – a 'problem' – and avoid the topic to escape embarrassment. Menstruation is inconvenient, messy and, for some women, painful and debilitating. There are calls for better education on the subject for both sexes to destigmatize and remove the negativity surrounding this most natural event.

vessels in the uterine wall, causing the thickened part of the lining to be devoid of oxygen and nutrients (ischemic) and die. Prostaglandins also cause the muscles of the uterus to contract to push this ischemic layer out, which can result in painful menstrual cramps. Day 1 of the cycle is denoted as the date when menstrual blood first appears.

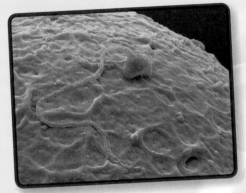

◀ *This is the moment a sperm cell reaches the ovum, frantically boring into the egg's surface in search of the nucleus.*

BOY MEETS GIRL

Sexual attraction between a man and a woman is often the first step on the long road to reproduction. Of course, in vitro fertilization and artificial insemination mean that the story does not have to start this way, but the traditional method is certainly the most common technique employed.

With sexual chemistry comes sexual arousal, which sees both male and female external genitalia engorged with blood. Male arousal starts when arteries in the penis receive the order to dilate, filling its two spongy tubes (corpus cavernosa) with blood and becoming rigid. The veins in the penis are compressed, which

prevents the blood from draining out of the shaft. During female arousal, the vagina secretes lubricating fluid to facilitate entry of the penis. Once the penis is inserted, the penis, vagina and clitoris rhythmically engage with each other and stimulate sensory receptors on the surface of each other's genitalia until an orgasm is achieved.

ORGASM

In men, orgasm results in the ejaculation of semen, which contains millions of sperm per 1 ml (0.03fl oz) of ejaculate. Anything lower than 15 million sperm per ml, or about 40 million sperm in a single ejaculate, is considered low. The amount of ejaculate ranges from 2 to 5ml (0.07 to 0.18fl oz). In women, an orgasm arises when the brain receives signals from the clitoris that cause the cervix to dip down and the vagina to contract or clasp around the penis. This ensures that it 'milks' as much sperm as possible.

FERTILIZATION (CONCEPTION)

Once inside the vagina, each sperm faces the ultimate race for life. Only those sperm capable of withstanding any

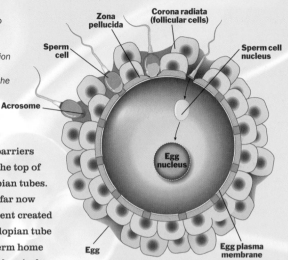

▶ Once a sperm cell has managed to penetrate the egg, the egg's surface hardens, preventing other burrowing spermatozoa from entering. Fertilization is complete when the nucleus of the sperm cell fuses with the nucleus of the egg and forms a zygote.

residual acidity and physical barriers such as the cervix, make it to the top of the corpus and enter the fallopian tubes. Those sperm that made it this far now swim against the wafting current created by the ciliated lining of the fallopian tube that pushes the egg along. Sperm home in on the egg with the help of chemical attractants released by the egg. Since the egg survives for only about 12 hours after it is released, time is critical.

The few successful sperm that reach the egg burrow through the outer layer until they reach a sugar-protein layer called the zona pellucida. Binding to this layer causes the release of enzymes from the acrosome of the sperm cell that enable it to bore through. Once a successful sperm penetrates the egg, a spectacular event known as the cortical reaction takes place: granules lining the inside of the zona pellucida release enzymes that cause it to instantly form cross-links across its surface and lock, preventing other sperm from entering.

Studies have shown that this moment of conception is associated with an increase in calcium inside the egg, which causes a release of zinc that has been captured on camera and illuminated as the 'zinc spark'.

ZYGOTE

When the nucleus of the sperm and egg unite, a zygote is formed. The sperm tail, which contains mitochondria, stays outside, and so the zygote retains the mitochondria and cytosol within the mother's egg. This explains why all your mitochondria are maternal in origin. This useful occurrence enables researchers to trace your ancestral lineage using maternal mitochondrial DNA.

ZYGOTE TO EMBRYO

Moral and spiritual debates rage about when actual life begins: at the moment of fertilization or the moment of birth. What is clear from science is that fertilization marks the point when a new human being starts to develop.

DIVIDING ZYGOTE

As the zygote travels along the fallopian tube, it divides by mitosis. It splits into two identical cells and continues on this trajectory until it forms a ball of cells known as a morula. Within a day or so, a fluid-filled cavity appears destined to become the amniotic sac. It changes the morula into a blastocyst, which has two layers: an outer layer that becomes the placenta and an inner layer that becomes the embryo. By now, the blastocyst has reached the uterus. Before it can embed itself in the uterine wall, it must get rid of the zona pellucida. It 'hatches' by disintegrating this protein layer surround.

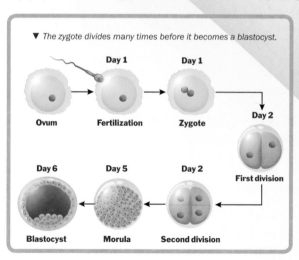

▼ *The zygote divides many times before it becomes a blastocyst.*

Ovum — Fertilization — Zygote — Day 1 — Day 1 — Day 2

First division — Second division — Morula — Blastocyst

Day 2 — Day 5 — Day 6

CORPUS LUTEUM

After ovulation, the ovarian follicle that housed the maturing egg gradually turns itself into a cyst-like structure called the corpus luteum. It produces the hormone progesterone (and a little oestrogen), which thickens the uterine wall and makes it more suited to receiving and supporting an embryo. In the absence of an embryo, the corpus luteum stops producing progesterone and the lining breaks down causing menstruation. The corpus luteum scars, which is why ovaries in a mature woman appear lumpy. If an embryo is present, the corpus luteum continues to produce progesterone until the placenta is fully formed and takes over.

IMPLANTATION

The time from conception to implantation in the uterine wall, or endometrium, is about 4 to 6 days. As the embryo burrows, it disturbs tiny blood vessels, causing some of the lining to dislodge and resulting in light bleeding or spotting a few days before a woman's period is due. This sometimes provides an early indication of pregnancy, although implantation bleeding does not always occur.

▼ *The implanted blastocyst enters the gastrulation phase about two weeks after fertilization, upon which three embryonic germ layers are formed.*

GASTRULATION

During the first few weeks, until the placenta is fully formed, the embryo gets most of its nourishment from the uterine lining. During this time, gastrulation occurs: the single-layered ball of cells becomes multilayered. This process takes place by switching on specific genes and turning off others. Gastrulation lays the foundations upon which structures and organs take form and develop from the three specific germ layers:

Ectoderm (outer layer): Forms the nervous system and most of the integumentary system.

Mesoderm (middle layer): Forms the musculoskeletal system, circulatory and lymphatic system, connective tissue and the genitourinary system.

Endoderm (inner layer): Forms most of the digestive system, the cells that line the respiratory tract and various glands.

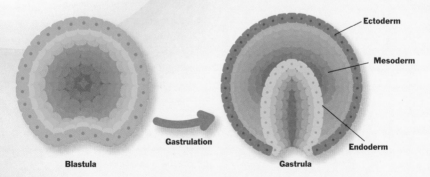

Blastula

Gastrulation

Gastrula

Ectoderm

Mesoderm

Endoderm

GROWING FETUS

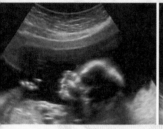 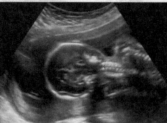 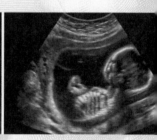

There is no universally agreed point at which an embryo becomes a fetus, but at around 8 to 9 weeks after conception, most of the foundations for the main organs and structures have been laid down and the embryo graduates to fetus status. Over the next few months, the organs take shape and grow larger.

▲ *Ultrasound scans of the growing fetus allow doctors to monitor how the baby is developing.*

THE PLACENTA

The placenta is a temporary organ that allows the fetus to receive nourishment directly from its mother's blood via the umbilical cord. It is shared between and controlled by both mother and fetus. The placenta is basically a mound of blood vessels that emerge from the embryo and intertwine with the blood vessels in the endometrium. Essential maternal nutrients and substances such as oxygen, glucose, amino acids and vitamins are exchanged for waste from the fetus without maternal and fetal blood ever mixing. If that happened, the mother's immune system would identify the fetus as non-self and reject it.

In addition, the placenta also serves as a major endocrine organ by releasing the hormone human chorionic gonadotropin (HCG) into the blood from 3–4 weeks into the pregnancy. HCG helps support the corpus luteum during the early stages to ensure it continues to release progesterone. It is HCG that is detected in pregnancy test kits.

AMNIOTIC FLUID

Amniotic fluid surrounds the fetus in the amniotic sac. Its purpose is to cushion the growing embryo and fetus as well as to help with the exchange of nutrients between mother and fetus. The fluid is initially a filtrate of maternal plasma and contains water, electrolytes, hormones, vitamins, carbohydrates and lipids. After week 10, it also contains fetal urine.

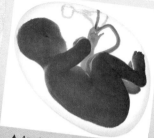

▲ Amniotic fluid protects the fetus from microbes due to its antibacterial properties.

FETAL DEVELOPMENT

Month 1

Month 2

Month 3

Month 4

Month 5

Month 6

Month 7

Month 8

Month 9

1st trimester

Months 1–2: A heartbeat is detected. Limbs form from buds, and digits begin to separate. The neural tube that gives rise to the central nervous system is formed.

Months 2–3: The urinary and circulatory systems are functioning, with waste going into the mother's blood via the placenta. By the end of the 3rd month, all organs are formed and the risk of miscarriage drops.

2nd trimester

Months 4–5: By the end of the 4th month, the genitals are fully formed. The fetus is capable of movement that can be felt (known as quickening).

Months 5–6: The fetus can respond to noises. Soft fine hair called lanugo covers the baby, along with a white coat of vernix that looks like cream cheese and protects the fetus's skin.

3rd trimester

Months 7–8: If the fetus were born at the end of the 7th month, there is a good chance of survival. The fetus can discriminate between light and dark and registers its mother's smell.

Months 8–9: The lungs complete in utero development. The baby moves less due to tight space. Finally, the head drops, or 'engages', into the pelvis ready for birth.

CHANGING MOTHER

During pregnancy, a mother changes both physically and mentally, compromising her own body to ensure she is fully prepared to cater for the needs of another. Hormones secreted by the placenta, including progesterone and oestrogen, induce changes to support and maintain gestation.

Hair: This stays in the growth anagen phase (see page 72) for longer due to the effects of pregnancy hormones.

Breasts: The breasts are one of the first structures to change. Oestrogen causes them to enlarge, while progesterone fully develops the milk-producing glands. The nipples also enlarge.

Heart: The heart works harder to manage the additional fluid and blood volume, which increases by 30 per cent or more. Swollen ankles, face, hands and feet are a common temporary occurrence. This increases the heart and pulse rate, and subsequently the breathing rate, to meet the additional oxygen demands of the fetus. The mother can also develop varicose veins from the growing uterus compressing on the inferior vena cava, which is the main vessel that carries blood from the lower limbs to the heart.

▶ *A pregnant woman's body is no longer under her direct control, as it changes to accommodate the needs of the growing fetus.*

Stomach: The growing fetus pushes the contents of the abdomen up, which pushes the stomach against the diaphragm. This results in frequent bouts of acid reflux, or heartburn, and occasional loud burps. Morning sickness occurs, particularly in the first trimester, due to changes in the levels of HCG. It can arise any time of the day. Food cravings are thought to be associated with nutritional deficiencies caused by the fetus's nutritional demands on the mother.

Bladder: This gets squashed by the growing fetus so fills quickly, leading to frequent visits to the lavatory.

Skin: Rapid weight gain causes the skin to stretch due to weakened collagen and elastin fibres.

Pelvis: Toward the later stages of pregnancy, the placenta releases the hormone relaxin, which relaxes the pelvic ligaments and causes the pelvis to widen and the birth canal to soften and open in preparation for birth.

Spine: Backache is a common symptom as the fetus grows. This is caused by the mother's centre of gravity shifting forward, putting extra strain on the muscles and joints of the lower spine as the mother leans back to counter the weight.

FUNDAL HEIGHT

The distance between your pubic bone and the top of your uterus, known as the fundal height, is used to estimate the stage of pregnancy. Between 16 and 36 weeks, the distance in centimetres is often the same as the number of weeks you have been pregnant. This measurement is often recorded by medical professionals as it can be a gauge of fetal growth and amniotic fluid development.

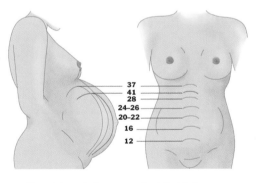

▲ Toward the end of pregnancy, fundal height becomes a less accurate measure of your baby's size.

293

HAPPY BIRTHING DAY

The day you were born was also the day your mother possibly went through extraordinary pain. For most mothers, the joy that comes from seeing and holding her new baby makes every moment of that pain worthwhile.

LABOUR

It is not called labour for nothing, because a mother has to work really hard to push out a baby, a task that can last anything from several hours to one or two days. The exact trigger for labour is not known, but by the 39th to 40th week (this number is slightly less the more babies a woman carries), a pregnancy has reached full term and labour will usually begin.

The experience of childbirth varies between women and between births, as no two are alike. Some labouring mothers get to the point where they have simply had enough and just want the baby out, with as much pain relief as possible: out go intricate birthing plans as well as some choice words aimed, usually, at the one who got them pregnant in the first place. For other women, it can be a wholly serene and spiritual experience supported with relaxing music and a warm birthing pool.

STAGES OF LABOUR

Water breaks (rupture of amniotic sac)	Prior to the waters breaking, the fetus's head presses against the mother's cervix, as substances called prostaglandins cause it to soften and relax. This dislodges the mucus plug that seals the cervix during pregnancy. When the amniotic sac breaks, also caused by pressure from the fetus's head, amniotic fluid starts to trickle out. Sometimes, the amniotic sac does not break prior to contractions starting.
Contraction and dilation	Muscles of the uterus contract to push the fetus's head against the cervix. This is the most painful and lengthy part of labour. Contractions cause the cervix to thin and open, or dilate. It is fully dilated when it reaches about 10cm (4in) in diameter.
Crowning	This is the moment when the fetus's head first becomes visible. The mother often has to control the urge to push, in order to synchronize it with powerful contractions.

BREASTFEEDING

▲ *Breastfeeding bestows significant health and emotional benefits to both mother and baby.*

As a newborn instinctively searches for a nipple to suckle, its mother's pituitary gland immediately releases the hormones prolactin and oxytocin, which trigger the production and release of milk from her breasts. Breastmilk provides the best fuel for rapid growth as it is nutritionally rich and has all the fluids and energy needed to survive for the first 4–6 months of life. It includes friendly bacteria, antibodies and immune cells. Breast milk also contains complex oligosaccharide sugar molecules that feed friendly gut bacteria called *Bifidobacterium*. These microbes coat the lining of the newborn's intestine, preventing the growth of harmful bacteria. This provides the necessary shield for your baby's immunity to develop. Benefits of breastfeeding to the mother include weight loss arising from the breakdown of body fats to make milk, and a reduced risk of breast cancer.

Birth	Babies are usually born head first, but may be born feet first if in breech position, or present in another strange order, which can cause complications. With the umbilical cord cut, the newborn is no longer connected to its mother and its circulatory and respiratory systems function independently. The baby lets out its first cry as the change in temperature shocks their brain and they take their first gasps of air. The blood vessels route themselves to collect oxygen from the lungs.
Afterbirth	The mother has to give birth again, this time to the placenta. Blood from the placenta is increasingly being collected and stored as it provides a valuable source of embryonic stem cells.

▲ *The umbilical cord is clamped and cut about 5 minutes after birth.*

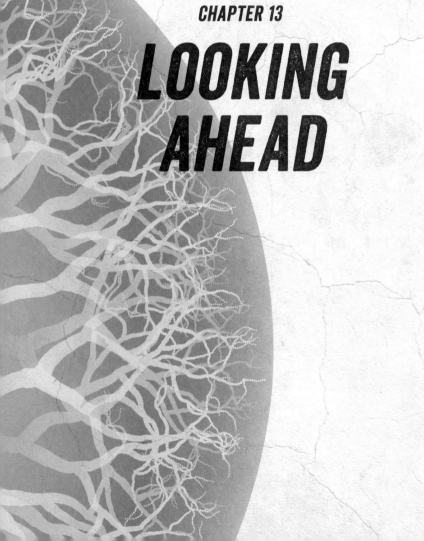

LOOKING AHEAD

21ST-CENTURY ANATOMY

▲ *Advances in technology make it possible to explore your anatomy like never before.*

Are recent technological advances in anatomical sciences removing the need for real-life operative experience and dissection? That is the worst fear of some medical professionals. Regardless of whether you are an early adopter, a luddite or a bit of both, one thing is for sure: these computer-based developments are here to stay, but they should only be adjunctive, educational and supportive.

Over the centuries, the need to physically look inside your body to understand what is going on has declined as medical imaging evolves as a vital preoperative, diagnostic and investigative tool. The medical application of computer-based technology has led to the development of 3D printing, which enables the reconstruction of near to exact model copies of your internal structures solely from radiographic images. This provides doctors and surgeons with information on your specific and unique anatomy and vital time to prepare their next move, which they previously would not have had in the operating theatre.

NEW TECHNOLOGIES

3D histology: Experts are creating 3D computer models of tissue using optically created serial tissue sections. This involves collecting different 2D image scans (slices) of the sample and stacking them on top of each other. The resulting 3D stack provides a better understanding of the spatial relationships between the cells and structures in the tissue. It is less labour and time intensive than the traditional method of using physical samples. It also provides an understanding of intact tissue whose architecture has been spared from damage.

Virtual reality simulators: This is where virtual reality meets computer-generated or real scanned cadavers. These simulators provide trainees and specialists with the opportunity to access an accurate, complete and dissectible human body that is multi-dimensional. It allows them to practise before engaging with cadavers or patients.

3D multi-media online resources: Today's anatomy software contains 3D images of realistic human body structures and organs. The images are embedded with animations, videos, instructions, essays and notes.

In addition, students can now receive computer-assisted instructions and learning, including multimedia 2D and 3D apps, plastinated structures and virtual reality simulators. Furthermore, the higher the resolving power of medical technologies, the greater the ability to discern complex morphologies and the delicate interface between diseased and non-diseased tissues.

Medical science is also evolving to target diseases at the nano-level using particles and machines so small (a billionth of a metre) that one can discriminate structures on the single cell and protein level. Indeed, nanomedicines already exist that use nanoparticles to transport drugs to cancer cells.

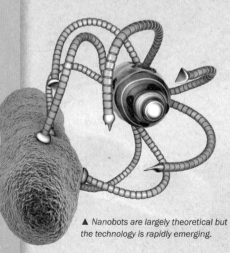

▲ Nanobots are largely theoretical but the technology is rapidly emerging.

◀ Dissection should be taught at an appropriate level during preclinical years of medicine and returned to at a more detailed level for specialist and surgical trainees.

DON'T FORGET TO DISSECT

With all these advances, the landscape of anatomy education is changing. In the past, students piled into the dissecting room or anatomy theatre and huddled around their master to observe his demonstration of dissection and discussion of the structures seen. This fairly passive approach to learning gross anatomy is known as prosection. It was only in recent times, following the emergence of preservatives such as formaldehyde, that students were able to dissect cadavers themselves. Prior to this, the demonstrator also had to be skilled enough to quickly dissect before the body started to putrefy.

With the advent of computer technologies and advanced simulation systems, today's students also have opportunities to learn anatomy via a plethora of digital-based platforms, with lectures, prosection and dissection kneaded into the mix. There is concern, however, that new technologies have reduced the time spent learning anatomy in the more traditional sense, through experiential learning via regional dissection. It is argued that this could have a knock-on effect on the expertise of doctors, surgeons and associated professions due to its direct connection to clinical practice. There are also worries that anatomy teaching is being supplanted by more molecular-based subjects, which have taken precedence as the reductive approach gains further hold of scientific inquiry.

BRINGING IT ALL TOGETHER

Clearly, there is no question that budding medical professionals, be they surgical or not, should be exposed to anatomical dissection. At the very least it provides that additional layer of confidence to visualize a disease they have seen first-hand in structures they have held.

In practice, a blended approach that combines level-appropriate traditional methods with its modern adjunct, punctuated with student-led study groups to aid engagement and build teamwork, appears to be the best way to stop any cracks from spreading across this field.

With all these reductive approaches driven by expensive technology, the future challenge will be bringing it all back on a systems level to understand how these processes and structures integrate.

Furthermore, it is vital one remembers that virtual reality simulators and 3D multimedia resources cannot replace traditional approaches, as most use organs and structures of a standard size and shape and are therefore limited by their inability to account for the range of anatomical variations that naturally exist within the population, something that can only be experienced in the real world (for more on this issue, see pages 308–11).

THE KINDNESS OF STRANGERS

Gone are the days when consent was not needed for cadaveric dissection. In the UK, the Anatomy Act of 1832 was superseded by the Tissue Human Act of 2004, while in the USA similar measures were taken with the Uniform Anatomical Gift Act, which stipulates that the use of cadavers is permitted only once consent has been given prior to death. Indeed, human dissection would cease to be possible if it were not for the kindness of strangers, who through true altruism and a love of humanity choose to bequeath their most precious gift, their body, to medical science. It is vital they are suitably commemorated for the personal sacrifice they have made in the name of helping us understand just how amazing the human body is.

REDRESSING THE BALANCE

In an age where male privilege is being held to task in many different sectors, it seems the field of anatomy is also in the crucible of this discourse.

While it is unfair to criticize the very important contributions men have made to our understanding of the human body, be they the doctors who first conceived scientific theories or the experimental subjects upon which those theories were tested, one cannot ignore that the knowledge acquired is skewed in favour of men. Historically, anatomical education used almost exclusively male cadavers. In the UK, this was largely a consequence of the Murder Act of 1752. Women were rarely convicted of murder and so were dissected only very occasionally. However, if the key differences between the sexes are the reproductive parts

▶ *Use of the masculine form as the default body type has stirred up key questions in anatomy and beyond.*

and these have been scrutinized equally for both sexes, what is the problem? The fact is that men and women differ not just in their genitals or breast tissue, but also in their musculoskeletal system, as well as hormonal and genetic factors, which all impact on health.

Most early stage clinical trials for new medications are also conducted in male volunteers, principally out of legitimate fears that a woman may harbour a hidden pregnancy or because it could affect her fertility in the long term (in contrast, men continually make new sperm). For this reason, clinical data are skewed in favour of men. Today, this imbalance is being redressed and has led to the development of programmes dedicated specifically to addressing women's health.

◀ *The female form is increasingly being represented in medical anatomical textbooks.*

◄ *Body Worlds exhibitions have brought anatomy into the public realm by depicting cadavers, known as 'spectaculars', in ordinary life-like poses.*

LOOKING INSIDE

To observe first-hand how a human looks on the inside has long been the province of the medical profession. Aside from wax museums, and specimens displayed in jars as historical artefacts, there was never any legal way of physically seeing what the innards of a real person looked like. Not until Body Worlds came along.

A travelling exhibition of gross anatomy spectacularized, Body Worlds is the brainchild of Dr Gunther von Hagens, a German anatomist who in the 1970s gave the world plastination, the process of immortalizing human tissue in chemical resins. Von Hagens' exhibits are rather like 3D versions of the illustrations of Vesalius, who was the first to depict the muscles and bones of human cadavers in life-like poses.

Von Hagens maintains that his goal is to educate the public about health and to showcase the vulnerabilities of the human body, by letting healthy and diseased organs that arise from unhealthy lifestyles be displayed side by side. Furthermore, his work sparks existential questions about the meaning of life and the differences between humans and animals, which are also exhibited. Despite this, some have questioned the ethics of these plastinates, which they feel have lost all human significance. The concern from most objectors is the issue of consent, but von Hagens assures that all those who donated their bodies have expressly permitted that they be immortalized in this way for educational purposes, an end that he also desires for himself.

UNSUNG HEROES

▲ Anna Morandi Manzolini's wax models were used to teach anatomy.

In any thorough analysis of the anatomical sciences of Western medicine, we cannot ignore the contributions that both women and minorities have made to the field, especially during those periods when societal structures and norms curtailed their abilities to contribute in similar capacities. Those who managed to overcome those barriers deserve special mention, for not only does doing so help to dispel falsities, stereotypes and myths, it also provides a source of inspiration for future generations of anatomists from underrepresented groups.

The Italian Alessandra Giliani (1307–26) is argued by some scholars to have been the first female anatomist in the western hemisphere, although the historical evidence for her existence is limited. Unusually for her era, she apparently received medical training at the University of Bologna, under the auspices of the professor Mondino de Liuzzi. As his assistant, she helped prepare cadavers for dissection. A truly gifted teenager, she is said to have devised her own technique to drain blood to aid visualization of the circulatory system.

In the 18th century, another Italian woman made her name in anatomy: Anna Morandi Manzolini (1716–74). Aged 20, she married Giovanni Manzolini, professor of anatomy at Bologna University, and gave birth to six children within the next five years. When her husband became ill with tuberculosis, she was given permission to give lectures in his place. At first partnering with her husband, she overcame her fear of dissection in order to learn anatomy. Her skills and knowledge grew exponentially until, after her husband's death in 1755, the university made her professor of anatomy in her own right. She excelled at producing extraordinarily accurate anatomical wax models, which were famous across Europe.

During the same period, the Frenchwoman Angélique du Coudray (c.1714–94) was a pioneering midwife who did much to reduce infant deaths in pre-Revolutionary France. She produced the midwifery textbook *Abridgment of the Art of Delivery*, which had illustrations detailing the relevant anatomy and surgical procedures. She also invented a lifesize obstetrical mannequin for practising mock births.

▲ *Angélique du Coudray's anatomical book saved lives.*

JAMES MCCUNE SMITH

Believed to be the first university-trained US physician of African descent, James McCune Smith (1813–65) was born into slavery. He was forced to travel to the United Kingdom to train because US universities denied him entrance on the basis of his race. He was accepted to study at the University of Glasgow in Scotland, and in 1837 obtained his medical degree after graduating top of the class.

Back in the United States, in 1843 Smith gave a series of lectures challenging the pseudoscientific practice of phrenology, which compared the anatomy and physiology of different races and attributed derogatory characteristics to people of African descent to justify discriminatory behaviours. Despite having a successful medical career, it is said that Smith was never accepted into national and local medical associations. In 2020, the University of Glasgow completed the £90.6 million James McCune Smith Learning Hub in his honour.

◀ *The University of Glasgow accepted Smith's application to study medicine.*

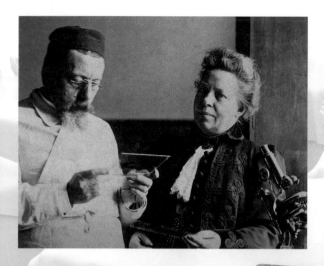

◀ Pioneering neuroanatomist Augusta Déjerine-Klumpke (seen here with her husband, Jules) had a strong interest in scientific research, but in her student years was repeatedly rejected for hospital externships because of her gender.

▼ Anatomist and scientist Florence Rena Sabin achieved many firsts, including being the first woman to become a professor (anatomy) at John Hopkins School of Medicine.

WOMEN OF THE MODERN AGE

Augusta Déjerine-Klumpke (1859–1927) was a US-born French neuroanatomist who was the first female intern to work in a Paris hospital. She co-wrote a book on the anatomy of the central nervous system and became the first female president of the French Neurological Society. She explained what is today called Déjerine-Klumpke paralysis, caused by an injury to the nerves controlling arm movement.

In the United States, Florence Rena Sabin (1871–1953) became the first woman to be elected to the US National Academy of Sciences, as well as the first female president of the American Association of Anatomists. Her neuroanatomy book is called Sabin's *Atlas of the Medulla and Midbrain*. Elizabeth Caroline Crosby (1888–1983) was also an esteemed US neuroanatomy lecturer. She co-authored the neuroanatomy textbook *Correlative Anatomy of the Nervous System*.

PROFESSOR DAME SUE BLACK

Your fingerprint is unique to you. Even if you have an identical twin who shares your DNA, your fingerprint will be different. Consequently, the use of fingerprints revolutionized criminal investigations. However, crime teams may soon be able to capture felons simply by looking at the shape of their hands.

H-unique is a European Research Community-funded project. It is being led by forensic anthropologist and leading anatomist Professor Dame Sue Black, of the UK's Lancaster University. Working with artists and forensic science researchers from the University of Dundee, as well as experts in anatomy, anthropology, genetics, bioinformatics and computer science, Black hopes to learn more about what makes a person's hands unique to generate forensic evidence that could be used in court.

But how is it possible to identify a criminal using images of their hands? 'We are all comfortable with the use of fingerprints,' Black explains, 'but there are many other aspects of anatomical variation, derived from different etiologies, that can be used, for example, superficial vein patterns, punctate pigmentation pattern, scar pattern, knuckle skin crease pattern.' These factors could be useful in, for example, apprehending perpetrators of child abuse whose hands have been identified from police photo evidence.

Black's team is collecting anonymous images of hands from the public, building a database that will provide a complete picture of the variation of hand traits that exists in a population. She hopes this will lead to the development of a computer algorithm that could search large datasets in record time. Clearly, the applications are vast and if successful this new biometric tool could assist crime prevention on a global scale.

◄ Sue Black hopes to find out whether the anatomy of your hand is sufficiently unique for forensic identification purposes.

VARIATIONS IN ANATOMY

Imagine a world where everyone looked the same, had identical features and was of similar shape and size. It certainly would make shopping for clothes a lot easier. However, thankfully, nature does not allow for such a thing, for the survival of every species depends on diversity and variation, both on a genetic and physical level. No matter what your anatomy is like, we are all unique and meant to be so. It is these variations that provide the basis upon which our anatomy has evolved.

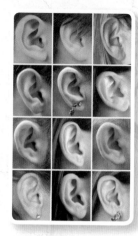

▲ The shape of your ears is as unique to you as your fingerprint.

Anatomical structures sit either within the normal range of variation and assume the label 'normal' or deviate from the accepted standard human anatomy as depicted in most textbooks. Such deviations, or anomalies (although outside the norm), can still be without issue, rendering the individual with nothing more than an interesting anatomical quirk. However, the line between what is considered normal and what is considered a defect or abnormality is extremely thin. Given that nature relies on throwing out aberrant constructs, one could argue these deviating morphologies are as natural and normal as nature itself.

CLINICAL IMPLICATIONS

Minor anatomical anomalies are generally compatible with life. Unless they are clearly obvious, they are often first detected randomly as an incidental finding during a medical examination for an unrelated condition or during cadaveric dissection. They fascinate the medical world because their embryological causal background provides insight into how the human body develops.

The most common anomalies arise in vascular structures, especially arteries. For example, some arteries have an extra branch, or diverging branches bifurcate at unexpected places. Similarly, the sciatic nerve normally divides low in the mid-thigh, but it can divide in the buttocks. Such anomalies can present clinical challenges and frustrations when it comes to conducting routine procedures and complex surgeries. For example, a surgeon's awareness of potential variations in coronary artery branches or in those in the circle of Willis is paramount to ensuring patient safety, and therefore the use of appropriate imaging techniques prior to surgery to detect them is often crucial. However, not all variations can be visualized, which can result in serious surgical outcomes.

In addition to determining the most appropriate surgical technique to apply, anatomical variations can influence the extent of symptoms a patient feels, as well as increase the risk of developing certain diseases and the course upon which they follow. Therefore, it is vital that medical professionals are trained to accommodate the structurally diverse nature of the human anatomy through different channels, such as cadaveric dissection, use of advanced imaging and clinical diagnostic technology, and collaborative resources that raise awareness of the significant anatomical variations that exist among humans.

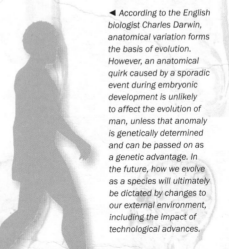

◀ According to the English biologist Charles Darwin, anatomical variation forms the basis of evolution. However, an anatomical quirk caused by a sporadic event during embryonic development is unlikely to affect the evolution of man, unless that anomaly is genetically determined and can be passed on as a genetic advantage. In the future, how we evolve as a species will ultimately be dictated by changes to our external environment, including the impact of technological advances.

SUPERNUMERARY

Having an extra body part that deviates from the body plan is more common than you think. It arises when a zygote begins to split but fails to fully complete the process, in the same way conjoined twins are formed. Exactly where the split had started will determine which body part is fully or partly replicated. Any organ system can be affected.

▼ The extra digit in a person with polydactyly is often less developed than the other digits on their hand or foot.

ORGAN SYSTEM	SUPERNUMERARY	EXAMPLE
Musculoskeletal	Additional muscles, tendons, limbs, bones and digits	Polydactyly is a condition where a person has one or more extra digits (toes or fingers). Digits that are fused due to failure of apoptosis is known as syndactyly.
Reproductive	Additional breast, penis, uterus, vagina or nipples, or having both male and female sex organs (intersex)	Polythelia is a condition where a person has supernumerary nipples. These grow along invisible milk lines that run in a V shape from the front of the armpits to the groin.
Digestive	Additional teeth	Hyperdontia is present in a small percentage of people. Extra teeth can occur in any place on the dental arch. Some people discover they have an extra set of canines hidden up in the maxilla only after routine dental X-rays.

HORSESHOE KIDNEYS

While some people are born with supernumerary kidneys or an extra ureter, a small percentage of the population have horseshoe kidneys that result from both kidneys fusing together at their lower lobes. In some individuals, horseshoe kidneys can be associated with pathological conditions, while others remain symptomless. These variations hold particular importance in the field of transplantation, which must be able to accommodate any anatomical variations that may exist.

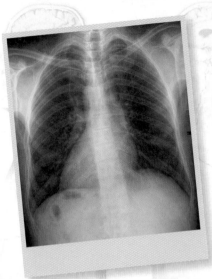

◀ This X-ray shows a patient with dextrocardia: the heart tilts to the right side instead of the left.

SITUS INVERTUS

This is an extremely rare condition in which the body's organs are reversed and mirror the normal position (situs solitus). For example, the heart normally tilts toward the left, but in situs invertus, or more specifically dextrocardia, it lies on the right side.

PALMARIS LONGUS

Situated in your forearm is the palmaris longus, the most variant human muscle. Not everyone has it and some people have only one. Its presence is indicated by its tendon, which is obvious in the middle of your inner forearm when you tense your arm and clench your fists. If you lack this muscle, it will not affect how your hand works or the strength of your grip, but if you have it then it can serve as a wonderful graft should you ever need a piece of muscle to put somewhere else.

▶ Not everyone has the palmaris longus muscle. Its tendon can be seen when you clench your fist.

INDEX

A

adipose tissue 68

adrenal gland 219, 229–30

adrenosine triphosphate (ATP) 236

aerobic respiration 103

ageing
  hair 73, 74
  musculoskeletal system 106–9
  neurons 205
  skin 69

albumin 130–1

allergic reactions 162

alveoli 176

amine hormones 227, 230

amniotic fluid 291

amygdala 208

anaerobic respiration 103

anaphylaxis 162

anatomical anomalies 308–9

anatomical planes 22

anatomical position 23

anatomists, great 17, 304–7

Anatomy Acts 19, 301

antibodies 153, 162, 163

antigens 144

anus 254

aorta 124

apocrine sweat glands 65

apoptosis 52–3, 108

appendix 254

arterial system 122–3, 124–5, 203, 309

arterioles 125

astrocytes 188, 193

atoms 27

ATP (adenosine triphosphate) 30, 103

B

autoimmune diseases 162–3

autonomic nervous system (ANS) 187, 216–19

axial skeleton 82–3

B-lymphocytes 151, 152–3, 155, 157

bacteria 147, 159, 249, 251
  gut 255, 295
  vaginal 283

basal ganglia 210–11

basement membrane 59

bile 249, 250

bile ducts 250

birth 294–5

Black, Professor Dame Sue 307

bladder 258, 264–5, 293

blood 112–37, 156
  heart and 114–21
  make-up of 129
  plasma 129, 130–1
  red blood cells (RBCs) 40–1, 129, 132–5, 148, 169, 224, 249, 267
  respiratory system and 180–1
  supply to the brain 203
  white blood cells 129, 135, 146, 148–51

blood–brain barrier (BBB) 193

blood pressure 136–7, 267

blood vessels
  arterial system 122–3, 124–5, 203, 309
  structure 123
  types of 122–3

venous system 122–3, 126–7

Body Worlds 303

bone marrow 132, 135, 145, 148, 157

bones 80–95
  ageing 106–7
  bone cells 41, 84, 85
  cartilage 90–1
  development 92–3
  make-up of 84–5
  shapes of 88–9
  types of 84, 86–7

Bowman's capsule 262–3

brain 46, 82, 189, 212
  blood supply to the 203
  cerebrum 194–5
  corpus callosum 204–5
  hemispheres and lobes 195
  hindbrain, midbrain and forebrain 196–9
  lobe functions 200–1
  protecting 192–3
  subcortical structures 206–9

brainstem 196–7

breasts 275, 292, 295
  breastfeeding 285, 295

breathing 168–9, 178–9, 245
  breathing rate 179

bronchi 171

bronchioles 171, 172–3

bulbourethral glands 279

C

cadavers 18–19, 301

calcium 267

cancellous bone 84, 86–7

capillaries 122–3, 125

respiratory system 168–83
respiratory tree 171
reticulocytes 134
ribcage 83
ribosomes 30–1, 41
RNA (ribonucleic acid) 34–5

S

Sabin, Florence Rena 306
saliva 243
scabs 160
Schwann cells 189
sebaceous glands 66, 144
sebum 66
Second World War 20–1
semen 278, 286
seminal vesicles 278
senses 220–1
sensory receptors 63
serum 131
sexual arousal 217, 286
sexual intercourse 286–7
sight 220
situs invertus 311
skeletal muscle 80
skeleton 80–1
  ageing 106–7
  axial 82–3
  skeletal muscles 96–9
skin 46, 56–69, 144, 293
  ageing 69
  colour 61
  dermis 57, 62–7, 69
  epidermis 57, 58–61, 62, 69
  hypodermis 68–9
skull 82
sleep 234–5
small intestine 247, 252–3
smelling 221
Smith, James McCune 305
smooth muscle 80, 113, 173
sneezing 182

snoring 182
software, anatomy 299, 301
specimens, anatomical 21
sperm 276–7, 278, 286–7
spinal cord 189, 212–15
spine 83, 293
stem cells 42–3, 45
steroids 226–7
stomach 233, 246, 293
subcortical structures 206–9
substantia nigra 198, 210
subthalamic nucleus 211
subthalamus 207
supernumerary 310
suprachiasmatic nucleus
  (SCN) 235
swallowing 244–5
sweat glands 64–5
sympathetic nervous system
  118, 216–18, 230
synapses 45, 100
synovial joints 94

T

T-lymphocytes 151, 152,
  154–7, 163, 224, 229
tasting 221
technology 298–301
teeth 242–3
temperature 236–7
tendons 80, 84, 99
terminology 22–3
testes 232–3, 274, 275, 276–7
testosterone 274, 281
thalamus 206–7
thymus 145, 157, 229
thyroid 157, 230–1
tissues 27, 44–5, 67
tongue 243
touching 221
trachea 171
transcription 34–5

U

urea 261
ureter 258, 264
urethra 258, 265, 279
urinary system 258–67
urine 266–7
uterus 282–3

V

vacuoles 31
vagina 282, 286
venous system 122–3, 126–7
vertebrae 83, 87
vertebrates 87
villi 252–3
virtual reality simulators
  299, 301
viruses 147
vitamin D 267

W

white blood cells 129, 135,
  146, 148–51
white matter 212
women
  anatomists 303–6
  birth 294–5
  male privilege 302
  menstrual cycle 284–5
  pregnancy 286–93
  puberty 272, 274–5
  reproductive system 270–1,
    280–3
  skeletons 89
wound-healing 160–1

Y

yawning 183

Z

zygote 287, 288

PICTURE CREDITS

All imagery copyright of Dreamstime.com, unless otherwise stated.

Every effort has been made to trace copyright holders and to obtain their permission for the use of copyright material. The publisher apologizes for any errors or omissions and would be grateful if notified of any corrections that should be incorporated in any future reprints or editions of this book.

Background images:
© Katsumi Murouchi/
123RF; © Sidmay/123RF

CHAPTER 9
p.232 © Designua/123RF
p.235 (T) © Jacopin/BSIP/
Science Photo Library
p.236 © Dr Ray Clark &
Mervyn Goff/Science
Photo Library

CHAPTER 10
pp.238–9 © Pikovit44/
Istockphoto.com
pp.240–1 (BG) © Engin
Korkmaz/123RF
p.240 © Monthian Ritchan-ad/
123RF
p.241 © QA International/
Science Source/Science
Photo Library
pp.246–7 (BG) © ChrisGorgio/
Istockphoto.com
p.250 © James Heilman, MD/
Wikimedia Commons
p.251 (BG) © Patrick
Guenette/123RF
p.252 © Guniita/123RF
p.253 © Dennis Kunkel
Microscopy/Science
Photo Library

Background images:
© Katsumi Murouchi/
123RF.com

CHAPTER 11
p.261 (T) © Maria
Gorbacheva/123RF
p.261 (B) © K H Fung/Science
Photo Library
p.263 © Jacopin/BSIP/Science
Photo Library
pp.265 © Alexmit/123RF

CHAPTER 12
pp.270–1 (BG) © Patrick
Guenette/123RF
p.270 (BR) ©
Andegro4ka/123RF
p.270 (BL) © Normaals/123RF
pp.272–3 (B) © A-Digit/
Istockphoto.com
p.274 © Peter Gardiner/
Science Photo Library
p.276 © Pixologicstudio/
Istockphoto.com
p.278 © Kocakayaali/
Istockphoto.com
p.286 © Thierry Berrod, Mona
Lisa Production/Science
Photo Library
pp.290–1 (BG) © Wellcome
Collection CC BY

p.292 © Johnwoodcock/
Istockphoto.com
p.293 © Florence Oll/BSIP/
Science Photo Library
Background images:
© Sidmay/123RF

CHAPTER 13
p.303 © Peter Menzel/Science
Photo Library
p.304 © Anna Manzolini/
Wellcome Collection/
Wikimedia Commons
p.305 (T) © J. Robert/
Wellcome Collection CC BY
p.305 (B) © Roger Griffith/
Wikimedia Commons
p.306 (T) © Wikimedia
Commons
p.306 (B) © U. S. National
Library of Medicine/Smith
College, Sophia Smith
Collection, Florence Rena
Sabin Papers
p.307 © Lancaster University
p.310 © Darryl Leja, NHGRI/
Wikimedia Commons
p.311 (T) © Nevit/Wikimedia
Commons

ENDMATTER
Greenvector/Istockphoto.com

ACKNOWLEDGEMENTS

First I would like to thank Professor Dame Sue Black, Pro-Vice-Chancellor for Engagement at Lancaster University, for very kindly taking the time to enlighten me on certain aspects of anatomy, including her current projects. I also wish to thank Dr Basaam Aweid, Consultant in Stroke Medicine, Hillingdon Hospital NHS Foundation Trust/Medical Director at Brunel University, for agreeing to review part of the chapter on the nervous system, and for introducing me to Professor Barry Mitchell, Emeritus Professor of Healthcare Sciences at De Montfort University, and previous Head of Anatomy at the University of Southampton Medical School, who cast his expert anatomical eye over this entire book. I am eternally grateful for all your help. Finally, I wish to thank my amazing partner, Nicky Dawe, for her unwavering support, patience, encouragement and understanding during construction of this book (you have been my rock) and my daughter Elodie for tolerating missing out on 'Daddy time'. Also, to my wonderful brothers and sisters, Joe, Viv, Jeff and Jen, for their patience and unconditional support, and to my Auntie Mabel for being mum, and the rest of my extended family in London and Dorset. And lest I forget those friends who always believed and continually motivated me from the start of this journey, I thank you with all my heart.

I would like to dedicate this book to my late parents, who I miss every single day. For Elizabeth Okona-Mensah and Kwasi Billings Okona-Mensah, without whom none of this would have been possible.

ALSO AVAILABLE IN THE SERIES:

Cracking Mathematics
Dr Colin Beveridge
ISBN: 9781844038626

Cracking Philosophy
Dr Martin Cohen
ISBN: 9781844038060

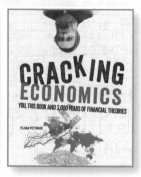

Cracking Economics
Tejvan Pettinger
ISBN: 9781844039319

Cracking Quantum Physics
Brian Clegg
ISBN: 9781844039494

Cracking the Elements
Rebecca Mileham
ISBN: 9781844039517

Cracking Neuroscience
Jon Turney
ISBN: 9781844039524